It's another great book from CGP...

Getting a top grade in GCSE Maths is no picnic. There are plenty of tough topics in the new exams that could trip you up on the day.

That's why we've made this brilliant book. It's packed with exam-style questions covering the most difficult parts of the course — if you can answer this lot, you won't get any nasty shocks in the exam.

We've also included fully-worked answers, so if you drop any marks, it's easy to find out exactly where you went wrong.

CGP — still the best! ☺

Our sole aim here at CGP is to produce the highest quality books — carefully written, immaculately presented and dangerously close to being funny.

Then we work our socks off to get them out to you — at the cheapest possible prices.

Contents

✓ Use the tick boxes to check off the topics you've completed.

Section Six — Pythagoras and Trigonometry

Section Seven — Probability and Statistics

Published by CGP

Editors:
Shaun Harrogate, Sarah Oxley, Alison Palin, Caley Simpson

Contributor:
Alastair Duncombe

With thanks to Jane Appleton, Rosie Hanson and Paul Jordin for the proofreading.

Clipart from Corel®
Printed by Elanders Ltd, Newcastle upon Tyne

Based on the classic CGP style created by Richard Parsons.

Text, design, layout and original illustrations © Coordination Group Publications Ltd. (CGP) 2015
All rights reserved.

Photocopying this book is not permitted, even if you have a CLA licence.
Extra copies are available from CGP with next day delivery • 0800 1712 712 • www.cgpbooks.co.uk

Exam Tips

Exam Stuff

1) For your GCSE Mathematics course you will have <u>three</u> exams — one non-calculator exam and two calculator exams.

2) Each exam is 1 hour 30 minutes long and is worth <u>80 marks</u>.

3) Timings in the exam are really important, so here's a quick guide...

- As each paper is worth <u>80 marks</u> and you've got <u>90 minutes</u> to complete the paper, you should spend about a <u>minute per mark</u> working on each question (i.e. 2 marks = 2 mins).
- The <u>hardest questions</u> will come towards the end of each exam and are often worth the <u>most marks</u>, so give yourself plenty of time to tackle them.
- Use any spare time at the end of the exam to <u>check</u> back through your answers and make sure you haven't made any silly mistakes. <u>Not</u> to just stare at that hottie in front.

Here are a Few Handy Hints

1) **Don't let <u>easy marks</u> slip through your fingers.**
   To give yourself the best chance of getting the highest grades you'll need to cut out as many <u>silly mistakes</u> as possible. <u>Read the question</u> properly, give your answer to the right <u>degree of accuracy</u>, give the <u>correct units</u> where needed and always <u>check your answer</u> is sensible.

2) **Show <u>each step</u> in your <u>working</u>.**
   You're less likely to make a mistake if you write things out clearly and in stages. Even if your final answer's wrong, you might pick up a few method marks if you've shown all your working.

3) **Look at the number of <u>marks</u> a question is worth.**
   If a question's worth 2 or more marks its probably going to require you to do a few steps. Make sure you write down what you're doing at each stage.

4) **Give <u>exact</u> answers when the question asks you to.**
   When you're asked for an <u>exact answer</u> you'll probably need leave your answer as a surd, in terms of π or as a fraction. <u>Don't round</u> at any stage in your calculation. If a <u>trig</u> question asks you for an exact answer, it's a big hint that you're going to have to use values of <u>common angles</u>.

5) **Learn the <u>formulas</u>.**
   Most of the formulas you'll need in your exams <u>won't</u> be given to you, so <u>learn them</u>.

> These handy hints might help you pick up a couple of extra marks — but they're no use if you haven't learnt the stuff in the first place. So make sure you revise well and do <u>as many</u> practice questions as you can.

Using Your Calculator

1) Before your exam, clear the memory of your calculator and check that it's in <u>degrees mode</u>. This is important for any <u>trigonometry</u> questions.

2) If you're working out a <u>big calculation</u> on your calculator, it's best to do it in <u>stages</u> and use the <u>memory</u> to store the answers to the different parts. If you try and do it all in one go, it's easy to mess it up.

3) If you're going to be a renegade and do a question all in one go on your calculator, use <u>brackets</u> so the calculator knows which bits to do first.

> REMEMBER: <u>The 2nd Handy Hint</u> still applies, even if you're using a calculator — you should still write down <u>all</u> the steps you are doing so the examiner can see the method you're using.

Fractions

1 In Jodie's school, one fifth of the pupils are in Year 7. The ratio of girls to boys in Year 7 is $3:2$, and 20% of the girls in Year 7 have blonde hair.

a) What fraction of the pupils in the school are girls in Year 7 with blonde hair?

....

[3]

b) State whether your answer to part a) would convert to a recurring decimal or to a terminating decimal. Explain your answer.

....

....

[1]

[Total 4 marks]

2 Look at the fraction sum below.

$$\frac{a}{11} + \frac{b}{6} = \frac{25}{33}$$

a) Work out the values of a and b, given that they are positive integers.

a = ..., b = ...

[3]

b) Write $\frac{25}{33}$ as a recurring decimal.

....

[2]

[Total 5 marks]

3 Add together $\frac{96}{180}$ and $1.14\dot{6}$. Give your answer as a mixed number in its simplest form.

....

[Total 5 marks]

4 Some square wall tiles have a side length of 2.2̇ cm.
Heather wants to cover an area of 1600 cm² with these tiles.

 Given that she can cover the area exactly with whole tiles,
work out the number of tiles she will need to use.

....
[Total 4 marks]

5 Which of the numbers below is biggest? Show how you get your answer.

 $0.1\dot{2}\dot{7}$, $\dfrac{38}{275}$, $\dfrac{160}{1375}$

Start by converting the decimal to a fraction.

....
[Total 4 marks]

6 Solve the equation below, giving your answer as a fraction in its simplest form.

 $\dfrac{7x-3}{6} = 0.0\dot{4}$

$x = $ ....
[Total 4 marks]

Score:

26

Bounds

1 Look at the formula below.

$$4z^3 = \frac{(x^{\frac{1}{2}}y^{-3}z)^2}{y^{-5}}$$

a) Rearrange the formula to make z the subject.

....
[3]

b) If $x = 6.8$ and $y = 1.2$, both rounded to one decimal place, work out the upper bound for z.
   Give your answer to 3 significant figures.

....
[3]

[Total 6 marks]

2 Shannon is performing in a gymnastics competition. Her overall score is calculated by adding together the scores for each piece of equipment. Her scores for each piece of equipment are shown below, correct to 4 significant figures. She has not done the vault yet.

      Floor: 16.42   Beam: 13.15   Bars: 14.88   Vault: ?

The current leader of the competition has a score of 60.15 to 4 significant figures.
After the vault, Shannon was in the lead by exactly 0.05 points.
What is the lowest possible score she could have got on the vault?

....
[Total 3 marks]

3 *A* and *B* are similar shapes.

$a = 6.2$ cm correct to the nearest 0.1 cm
$b = 3.5$ cm correct to the nearest 0.1 cm
$c = 11.8$ cm correct to the nearest 0.1 cm

Calculate the minimum possible value for the length *d*.

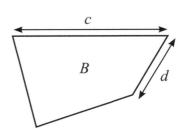

Scale factor = new length ÷ old length

.... cm
[Total 4 marks]

Section One — Number

4 The circle opposite represents a pizza.
The shaded sector shows a slice of pizza with area S cm².

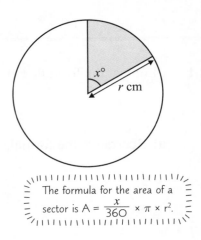

$S = 179.2$ correct to 1 decimal place.
$x = 60$ correct to the nearest whole number.
The length r cm is the radius of the pizza.

Find the lower and upper bounds for the radius of the pizza.
Give your answers to 2 decimal places.

The formula for the area of a sector is $A = \dfrac{x}{360} \times \pi \times r^2$.

Lower bound .... cm

Upper bound .... cm

[Total 5 marks]

5 The diagram shows a triangle with area A cm².

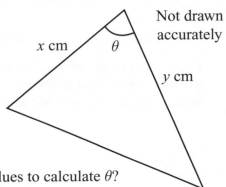

Not drawn accurately

$A = 2900$ to 2 significant figures.
$x = 97.0$ to 3 significant figures.
$y = 78.9$ to 3 significant figures.

θ is an acute angle.
The value of θ can be found using this formula: $\sin \theta = \dfrac{2A}{xy}$

What is the maximum possible error if you use the rounded values to calculate θ?
Give your answer to 3 significant figures.

Work out the lower and upper bounds for θ and compare them to the calculation using the rounded values.

.... °

[Total 7 marks]

Score:

25

Section One — Number

Standard Form

1   Express $(3 \times 10^{11})^4$ in standard form.

....

[Total 2 marks]

2   The area of a national park is 6.4×10^5 acres. 65% of the park is woodland, and three-quarters of the woodland is protected.

Work out the area of woodland that is NOT protected.
Give your answer as an ordinary number.

.... acres

[Total 3 marks]

3   Write $\dfrac{25^2 \times 6}{2^2 \times 50^4}$ in standard form.

....

[Total 3 marks]

4   A shipping container has a weight of 4.2×10^4 N to 2 significant figures.
The area of the base of the shipping container is 30 m² to 1 significant figure.

The deck of a cargo ship has a pressure restriction of 1600 N/m². Is it safe for the shipping container to be transported on the cargo ship? Show working to support your answer.

Pressure = force ÷ area

....

....

[Total 3 marks]

8

5 The Heron Sea has a volume of 1.4×10^{14} litres, of which 12% is salt.
The Cobalt Sea has a volume of 8.5×10^{12} litres, of which 8% is salt.

What is the percentage decrease in the volume of salt from the Heron Sea to the Cobalt Sea?
Give your answer to 2 decimal places.

.... %

[Total 3 marks]

6 A newspaper claims that the mass of muffins eaten in the world last year was 1.8×10^{12} kg.
Given that there are approximately 7.2 billion people in the world and the average mass of a
muffin is 120 g, do you think the newspaper is correct? Show working to support your answer.

1 billion = 1 000 000 000

....

....

....

[Total 4 marks]

7 $a = 2^{10} \times 5^9$, $b = 9\,000\,000$, $c = 2.4 \times 10^9$
Work out the lowest common multiple of a, b and c.

Give your answer in standard form.

....

[Total 4 marks]

Score:

22

Section One — Number

Powers

1 Find an approximate value of $111^{\frac{1}{4}} \times 111^{\frac{1}{4}}$ to 3 significant figures.

....

[Total 2 marks]

2 Find the exact value of $81^{\frac{3}{4}}$.

....

[Total 2 marks]

3 Simplify fully $a^7 \times (25a^6 b^{10} c^5)^{\frac{1}{2}}$.

....

[Total 2 marks]

4 Find the value of $125^{\frac{1}{3}} \times 3^{-2}$. Give your answer as a recurring decimal.

....

[Total 3 marks]

5 Evaluate $\left(\frac{64}{27}\right)^{-\frac{1}{3}}$. Give your answer as a fraction in its simplest form.

....

[Total 2 marks]

6   Given that $\left(\dfrac{729}{8x}\right)^{\frac{1}{3}} = \dfrac{9}{4}$, find the value of x.

$x =$ ....
[Total 2 marks]

7 $a = 3b^3 + 2b^6$, where $b = (4c + 3)^{\frac{1}{3}}$

Express a in terms of c, simplifying your answer as much as possible.

....
[Total 3 marks]

8   Find the values of x and y, given that $\left(\dfrac{64}{49}\right)^{-\frac{x}{y}} = \dfrac{343}{512}$.

$x =$ .... , $y =$ ....
[Total 3 marks]

9   Evaluate $\dfrac{\left(2\frac{7}{9}\right)^{-\frac{1}{2}} \times 3\frac{1}{3}}{2^{-2}}$.

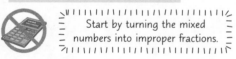
Start by turning the mixed numbers into improper fractions.

....
[Total 5 marks]

Score:

24

Surds

1 Simplify the expression $\sqrt{2} + (\sqrt{2})^2 + (\sqrt{2})^3 + (\sqrt{2})^4 + (\sqrt{2})^5$.

....

[Total 3 marks]

2 Write $\sqrt{343} + \dfrac{21}{\sqrt{7}} - 4\sqrt{252}$ in the form $a\sqrt{b}$, where a and b are integers.

....

[Total 4 marks]

3 Find the exact length of side a in the triangle on the right.

Give your answer in its simplest form.

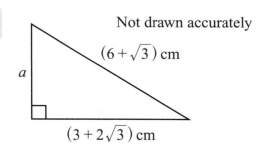

Not drawn accurately

$(6 + \sqrt{3})$ cm

a

$(3 + 2\sqrt{3})$ cm

$a = $ .... cm

[Total 4 marks]

4 Expand and simplify $(\sqrt{5} - 6)^3$. Give your answer in the form $a + b\sqrt{5}$.

....

[Total 3 marks]

12

5 Find the exact volume of the cuboid on the right.

Give your answer in the form $a + b\sqrt{5}$, where a and b are integers.

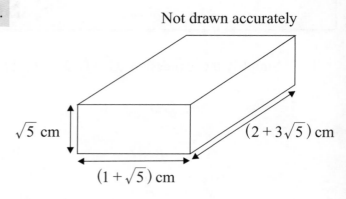

Not drawn accurately

$\sqrt{5}$ cm

$(2 + 3\sqrt{5})$ cm

$(1 + \sqrt{5})$ cm

.... cm³

[Total 4 marks]

6 Simplify $\dfrac{2\sqrt{3}}{3+\sqrt{3}} + \dfrac{2+\sqrt{3}}{2-\sqrt{3}}$.

You should start by rationalising the denominator of each fraction.

....

[Total 5 marks]

7 Simplify $\dfrac{(1+2\sqrt{2})^2}{\sqrt{2}-1}$.

....

[Total 4 marks]

Exam Practice Tip

No doubt about it — surds are tricksy little devils. Always remember to simplify your answers as much as possible — if you have a big number in a surd, see if it'll divide by a square number to simplify it some more. The smaller the surd, the easier it is to deal with — especially if you're trying to combine a few different surds.

Score

27

Section Two — Algebra

Quadratic Equations

1   The surface area of a sphere is $36\pi x^2 + 48\pi x + 16\pi$ cm^2,
where x is positive. Find the radius of the sphere in terms of x.

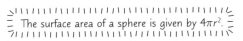
The surface area of a sphere is given by $4\pi r^2$.

.... cm

[Total 3 marks]

2   Look at the quadratic equation $2x^2 - 3x - 35 = 0$.

a) Fully factorise the expression $2x^2 - 3x - 35$.

....

[2]

b) Use your answer to part a) to solve the equation $2(2x - 1)^2 - 3(2x - 1) - 35 = 0$.

$x = $ .... or $x = $ ....

[3]

[Total 5 marks]

3   Solve the equation $\dfrac{x}{2x + 1} - \dfrac{x + 3}{x - 1} = 2$.

$x = $ .... or $x = $ ....

[Total 4 marks]

Section Two — Algebra

4 Look at the quadratic equation $3x^2 - 14x - 24 = 0$.

a) Fully factorise the expression $3x^2 - 14x - 24$.

....

[2]

b) Use your answer to part a) to solve the equation $3x^2 - 14x - 24 = (3x + 4)^2$.

Remember — you're looking for two solutions here.

$x = $ .... or $x = $ ....

[4]

[Total 6 marks]

5 The surface area of a cylinder with height 1 m is 31π m². Find r, the exact radius of the cylinder in its simplest form.

The surface area of a cylinder is given by $2\pi rh + 2\pi r^2$.

$r = $ .... m

[Total 4 marks]

6 Calculate the positive value of $\dfrac{1}{1 - 3x}$ if $\dfrac{1}{x} + \dfrac{6}{x + 2} = 5$.

$x = $ ....

[Total 5 marks]

Score:

27

Section Two — Algebra

Completing the Square

1 Write the expression $x^2 + 7x + 11$ in the form $(x + a)^2 + b$.

....

[Total 3 marks]

2 $f(x) = x^2 + px + q$. The graph of $y = f(x)$ has a turning point at $(2, 5)$, as shown below.

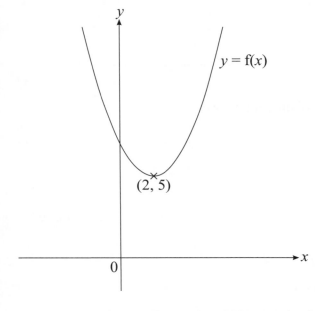

$(2, 5)$

a) Find the values of p and q.

$p =$ .... and $q =$ ....

[3]

b) Hence, or otherwise, find the turning point of the graph of $y = f(x - 2) - 3$.

> Use the completed square form of f(x).

....

[2]

c) On the axes above, sketch the graph of $y = f(x - 2) - 3$, labelling the coordinates of the turning point.

[2]

[Total 7 marks]

3 $3x^2 + sx + 29$ can be written in the form $r(x + 4)^2 + t$, where r, s and t are integers.

By finding the values of r, s and t, work out the coordinates of the turning point of the curve $y = 3x^2 + sx + 29$.

....

[Total 4 marks]

4 A curve has equation $y = x^2 + px + q$. The curve has a minimum point at $(4, 7)$.

Show that the curve passes through the point $(11, 56)$.

[Total 2 marks]

5 A curve has equation $y = 3x - x^2 + 5$.

a) Find the turning point of the curve.

....

[3]

b) Is this turning point a maximum or minimum? Explain your answer.

....

....

[1]

[Total 4 marks]

6 Look at the quadratic equation $5x^2 + 20x + 12 = 0$.

a) Write the expression $5x^2 + 20x + 12$ in the form $u(x + v)^2 + w$.

....

[4]

b) Hence find the solutions of $5x^2 + 20x + 12 = 0$. Give your answers to 3 significant figures.

$x =$ .... or $x =$ ....

[2]

[Total 6 marks]

Exam Practice Tip

Completing the square can be really nasty — but remember, you can always check your answer by expanding your completed square form and checking that you end up with the original equation. It's easy to make mistakes when there are a load of awkward fractions flying around, so take your time and don't rush or panic.

Score

26

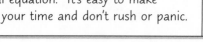

Algebraic Fractions

1   Simplify fully $\dfrac{2v^2 - 18}{v^2 + 3v} \times \dfrac{v^2 - v}{v^2 + 8v - 9}$.

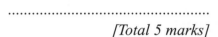

[Total 5 marks]

2   Let $a = 5x^2 - 80y^2$ and $b = 40y - 10x$. Find an expression for $\dfrac{1}{a} \div \dfrac{1}{b}$.

Give your answer in its simplest form.

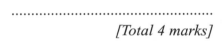

[Total 4 marks]

3   Write $\dfrac{3}{x} + \dfrac{2x}{x + 4}$ as a single fraction.

[Total 3 marks]

4   Simplify fully $\dfrac{x + 7}{x^2} \times \dfrac{x^2 + 2x}{x^2 - 49} \times \dfrac{6x - 42}{3x + 6}$.

[Total 5 marks]

Section Two — Algebra

18

5   Write $\frac{1}{x^2} + \frac{x+3}{x-2} - \frac{4}{x}$ as a single fraction.

....

[Total 4 marks]

6   Simplify fully $\frac{x^2-5}{2x^2-7x-4} \times \frac{2x+1}{x-\sqrt{5}}$.

Watch out — $x^2 - 5$ is a difference of two squares.

....

[Total 3 marks]

7   Prove that $\frac{14x-35}{2x^2+x-15} \div \frac{4xy-12y}{2x^2y-18y} \equiv k$, where k is a number to be found.

[Total 6 marks]

Score:

30

Sequences

1 The nth term of a sequence is $\left(\frac{1}{2}\right)^n$.

Find the difference between the 5th and 8th terms in the sequence.

....
[Total 2 marks]

2 Imogen and Justin each think of a sequence. Imogen's sequence is an arithmetic sequence with nth term $93 - 6n$. Justin's sequence is quadratic and starts 3, 9, 21, 39, ...

a) Find an expression for the nth term of Justin's sequence.

....
[3]

b) Find the only term that is the same in both sequences.

....
[3]
[Total 6 marks]

3 A quadratic sequence has nth term $3n^2 - 4n + 1$.
The sum of two consecutive terms in the sequence is 581.

What are the two terms?

.... and ....
[Total 5 marks]

4 The first, second and third terms of an arithmetic sequence are $6x + 1$, $8x - 29$ and $5x + 6$, where x is an integer.

Find the 20th term in the sequence.

In an arithmetic sequence, the difference between each consecutive pair of terms is the same.

....
[Total 6 marks]

5 A sequence has nth term $50 - \frac{1}{2}n^2$. Find the value of the first term in the sequence that is less than 0.

Don't use trial and error here — set up and solve a quadratic inequality.

....
[Total 3 marks]

6 Kim and Alex each think of a sequence.

Kim's geometric sequence:

nth term $= (\sqrt{3})^n$

Alex's quadratic sequence:
First three terms are
18, 21, 27

Show that the sum of the 8th term of Kim's sequence
and the 6th term of Alex's sequence is a square number.

You don't have to work out the nth term of Alex's sequence as you only need to go as far as the 6th term.

[Total 4 marks]

Score:

26

Section Two — Algebra

Quadratic Inequalities

1   Solve the inequality $x^2 + x - 56 < 0$.

....

[Total 3 marks]

2   Look at the grid on the right.

On the grid, shade the region(s) that satisfies the inequalities below:
$$y \leq 3$$
$$y + x \leq 5$$
$$4x - x^2 \leq 0$$

[Total 4 marks]

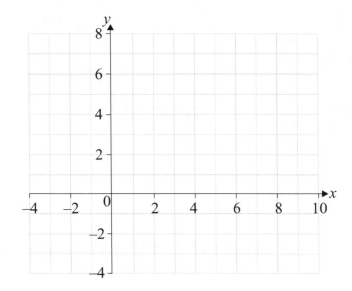

3   The sum of the areas of the circles below is greater than 160π cm^2.

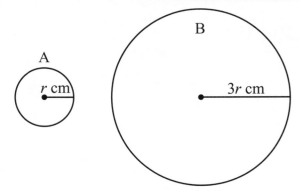

Given that r is an integer, find the smallest possible radius of each circle.

radius of circle A = ... cm, radius of circle B = ... cm

[Total 3 marks]

Section Two — Algebra

4   Solve the inequality $3x^2 - x - 90 \geq 5x + 15$.

....

[Total 4 marks]

5   Look at the two cuboids below. The volume of cuboid B is greater than the volume of cuboid A.

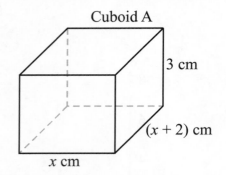

Cuboid A

3 cm

$(x + 2)$ cm

x cm

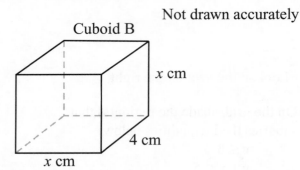

Not drawn accurately

Cuboid B

x cm

4 cm

x cm

a) Show that $x^2 - 6x > 0$.

[3]

b) If x is an integer, find the smallest possible volume of cuboid B.

.... cm^3

[4]

[Total 7 marks]

6   Solve the inequality $x^2 \leq \dfrac{23x - 45}{2}$.

....

[Total 4 marks]

Exam Practice Tip

It's always a good idea to very quickly sketch the quadratic graph to work out which bit of it you want (either above or below the x-axis, depending on the inequality sign). This will tell you whether you want a solution within an enclosed region (e.g. $-1 < x < 1$) or a solution in two separate bits (e.g. $x < -1$ and $x > 1$).

Score

25

Section Two — Algebra

Iterative Methods

1 The graphs of $y = (x - 1)^2(2x + 5)$ and $y = 10x^2 - 8x - 2$ intersect three times.

a) Show that one of the points of intersection occurs at $x = 1$.

[2]

b) Show that, at the points of intersection, $2x^3 - 9x^2 + 7 = 0$.

[3]

c) Hence show that, for one of the points of intersection, the value of x lies between 4 and 5.

[2]

d) By filling in the table below, find an approximation to the solution of $2x^3 - 9x^2 + 7 = 0$ to 1 d.p. You might not need to use all the rows.

x	$2x^3 - 9x^2 + 7$	
4	−9	
5		Positive
4.1	−6.448	
4.2		

$x = $ ....

[4]

[Total 11 marks]

24

2 The equation $x^3 + 3x^2 - 5 = 0$ has one solution.

a) Show that the solution of $x^3 + 3x^2 - 5 = 0$ lies between 1 and 1.5.

[2]

b) The formula $x_{n+1} = x_n - \dfrac{x_n^3 + 3x_n^2 - 5}{3x_n^2 + 6x_n}$ can be used to solve $x^3 + 3x^2 - 5 = 0$.

Starting with $x_0 = 1$, find the solution to the equation $x^3 + 3x^2 - 5 = 0$ to 5 decimal places.

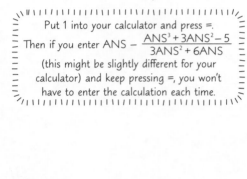

Put 1 into your calculator and press =.
Then if you enter ANS $- \dfrac{\text{ANS}^3 + 3\text{ANS}^2 - 5}{3\text{ANS}^2 + 6\text{ANS}}$
(this might be slightly different for your calculator) and keep pressing =, you won't have to enter the calculation each time.

$x = $ ....

[3]

[Total 5 marks]

3 The equation $x^3 - 3x^2 - 4x + 10 = 0$ has three solutions.

a) The equation can be rearranged as $x = \pm\sqrt{\dfrac{ax - 10}{x - b}}$.
Show that $a = 4$ and $b = 3$.

[3]

b) The formula $x_{n+1} = \sqrt{\dfrac{4x_n - 10}{x_n - 3}}$ can be used to solve $x^3 - 3x^2 - 4x + 10 = 0$.

Starting with $x_0 = 1.5$, find one solution to the equation $x^3 - 3x^2 - 4x + 10 = 0$ to 3 significant figures.

$x = $ ....

[3]

[Total 6 marks]

Score:

22

Section Two — Algebra

Simultaneous Equations

1   Solve the following pair of simultaneous equations.

$$x^2 + 4y^2 = 37$$
$$2x - y = x + 4$$

$x =$ .... , $y =$ ....

and $x =$ .... , $y =$ ....

[Total 5 marks]

2   The shape below is made up of two rectangles with dimensions as shown.
The total area of the shape is 83 cm², and the total base length is 9 cm.

Find the values of x and y, given that they are both integers.

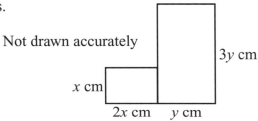

Not drawn accurately

$3y$ cm

x cm

$2x$ cm y cm

$x =$ .... , $y =$ ....

[Total 5 marks]

3   The line $7x - y = 25$ intersects the circle $x^2 + y^2 = 25$ at two points, *A* and *B*.
Find the exact length of the line *AB*. Give your answer in its simplest form.

....

[Total 6 marks]

Section Two — Algebra

4   The cuboid below has a weight of 120 N. When the cuboid rests on face *A*, the pressure exerted is 10 N/m². When the cuboid rests on face *B*, the pressure exerted is 7.5 N/m².

Find the volume of the cuboid.

Not drawn accurately

Use the formula pressure = force ÷ area to form two simultaneous equations.

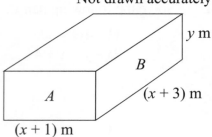

.... m³

[Total 6 marks]

5   The line $y = 2x - 5$ intersects the curve $y = -x^2 + 15x - 41$ at the points *A* and *B*, as shown.

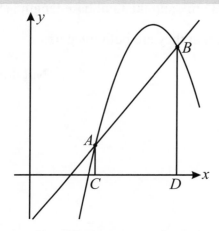

C and *D* are points on the *x*-axis. The lines *CA* and *DB* are parallel to the *y*-axis.
Calculate the area of the quadrilateral *ABDC*.

.... units²

[Total 6 marks]

Exam Practice Tip

Remember, you can always check your x- and y-values by putting them back into the original equations and checking they produce the numbers given in the question. If they don't, you've gone wrong somewhere. Check your factorising — it's easy to make a mistake (especially with tricky numbers).

Score

28

Section Two — Algebra

Proof

1 Prove that $(2n + 1)^3 - 1 \equiv 2n(4n^2 + 6n + 3)$.

[Total 3 marks]

2 Prove that the product of three rational numbers is always rational.

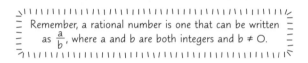

Remember, a rational number is one that can be written as $\frac{a}{b}$, where a and b are both integers and b ≠ O.

[Total 2 marks]

3 If a and b are both odd, prove that $(a + b)^{40}$ is even.

[Total 2 marks]

4 Prove that the sum of any three consecutive cube numbers is a multiple of 3.

[Total 4 marks]

Section Two — Algebra

5 Max thinks of a whole number that is one more than a multiple of 5.
Samira thinks of the number that is four less than Max's number.

Prove that the difference in the squares of their values is a multiple of 8.

[Total 5 marks]

6 Show that $3^8 - 7^4$ is a multiple of 13.

[Total 3 marks]

7 Show that the sum of 15^{12} and 12^{16} is a multiple of 9.

╲│││││││││││││││││││││││││╱
Start by writing 15^{12} and 12^{16} as
products of their prime factors.
╱│││││││││││││││││││││││││╲

[Total 3 marks]

Score:

22

Section Two — Algebra

Functions

1 $f(x) = \sqrt{2x - 8}$ $(x \geq 4)$ and $g(x) = x^2 + 4.$

a) Find the exact value of fg(4). Give your answer in its simplest form.

....
[2]

b) Find gf(x).

gf(x) = ...
[2]

c) Find the inverse function $f^{-1}(x)$.

$f^{-1}(x)$ = ...
[3]

[Total 7 marks]

2 $f(x) = \dfrac{x + 5}{2}$ and $g(x) = 3x - 10.$

Find the value of x for which $f^{-1}(x) = g^{-1}(x)$.

x = ...
[Total 6 marks]

3 $f(x) = 2x - 1$ and $g(x) = \sin x.$

Find both solutions to the equation fg(x) = 0 for $0° \leq x \leq 360°$.

> A quick sketch of the graph of y = sin x will help you find the second x-value.

x = ...° and x = ...°
[Total 4 marks]

Section Two — Algebra

4 $f(x) = x^2 + 4x + 3$ and $g(x) = x + 2$.

a) Find $fgg(x)$.

$fgg(x) =$ ....

[3]

b) Solve the equation $fgg(x) = 0$.

$x =$ .... or $x =$ ....

[2]

[Total 5 marks]

5 $f(x) = 3x + 1$, $g(x) = x^2 + 3x$ and $h(x) = x^3$.

Find $fgh^{-1}(x)$.

$fgh^{-1}(x) =$ ....

[Total 4 marks]

6 $f(x) = \dfrac{4x}{x+9}$ $(x \neq -9)$ and $g(x) = 2x + 1$.

Solve the equation $fg(x) = x$.

$x =$ .... or $x =$ ....

[Total 5 marks]

Exam Practice Tip

Don't be put off if you have to solve things in function questions. Just put in the expression you know for the function (you might have to work it out first if it's a composite or inverse function), then solve it like a normal equation. And in composite functions, always remember to do the function closest to x first.

Score

31

Section Two — Algebra

Coordinates and Ratio

1   The line segment AB is shown below. M is the midpoint of AB and has coordinates (4, 5).

The coordinates of point A are (–2, 2).
a) Find the coordinates of point B.

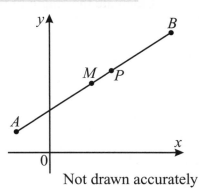

Not drawn accurately

(...................... , ...)
[2]

Point P lies on the line segment AB such that $MP:PB = 1:2$.
b) Find the ratio $AP:AB$.

....
[3]

[Total 5 marks]

2 $ABCD$ is a square with side length 4 units. The coordinates of point D are (2, –1).
M is the centre of the square and point E has coordinates (0, 5).

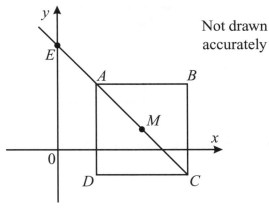

Not drawn accurately

Find the ratio $EM:MC$. Give your answer in its simplest form.

....

[Total 3 marks]

3 The diagram shows rectangle *ABCD*. Point *E* has coordinates (0, –4), point *F* has coordinates (6, 0) and point *B* has coordinates (6, 4).

Not drawn accurately

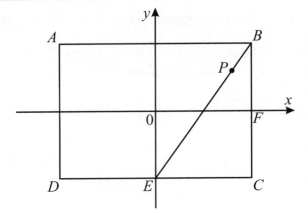

P is the point on the line *EB* such that *EP* : *PB* = 3 : 1.
Calculate the length of the line segment *PF*.

....

[Total 4 marks]

4 *ABCD* is a parallelogram. The coordinates of point *A* are (–2, 7) and the coordinates of point *D* are (–5, 2). *M* is the midpoint of line *AC* and has coordinates (3, 4.5).

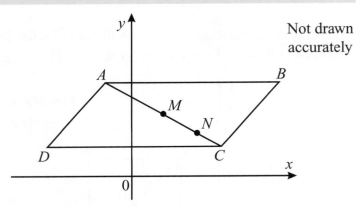

Not drawn accurately

Point *N* lies on the line *AC* such that *AM* : *MN* : *NC* = 5 : 3 : 2.
Find the exact length *NB*.

....

[Total 6 marks]

Score:

18

Perpendicular Lines

1   Line L_1 passes through the points $(4, 6)$ and $(11, 20)$.
Line L_2 is perpendicular to L_1 and intersects the x-axis at $(28, 0)$.

Find the equation of line L_2.

....
[Total 3 marks]

2   The line SQ is a diagonal of the kite $PQRS$ and has equation $y = 4x - 3$.
The coordinates of point R are $(8, 15)$. Find the equation of the other diagonal PR.

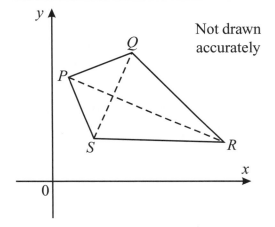

Not drawn accurately

....
[Total 3 marks]

3   Lines L_1 and L_2 are perpendicular and intersect at point M.
L_1 has equation $x + 5y = 100$ and L_2 passes through point $(2, 4)$.

Find the coordinates of point M.

(................... , ...)
[Total 5 marks]

Section Three — Graphs

4   The line L_1 has equation $2y - x = 14$ and passes through the points $P(6, 10)$ and Q. L_2 is the line that is perpendicular to L_1 and passes through point P. L_2 intercepts the y-axis at R. RQ is horizontal.

Find the coordinates of Q.

Not drawn accurately

(.................... , ...)

[Total 5 marks]

5   Lines L_1 and L_2 are parallel. L_1 has equation $2x + 3y = 12$ and L_2 passes through point $(6, 13)$. Line L_3 is perpendicular to L_1 and L_2 and intersects L_1 at $(3, 2)$.

Find the coordinates of the point of intersection of L_2 and L_3.

(.................... , ...)

[Total 6 marks]

Exam Practice Tip

Remember — the gradients of two perpendicular lines multiply to give −1. Once you know that, use whatever information you're given to find the equation of the line. You sometimes have to do quite a bit of work to find the equation, so if you're asked to find a point, don't forget to do the final step and find the coordinates.

Score

22

Harder Graphs

1 The graph shows the curve $y = \dfrac{9}{x}$.

Find the smallest possible distance between the two sections of the graph. Give your answer as a simplified surd.

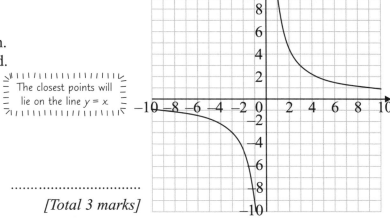

The closest points will lie on the line $y = x$.

....

[Total 3 marks]

2 The point (7, 24) lies on a circle with centre (0, 0). Find the radius and equation of the circle.

Radius = ...

Equation: ....

[Total 2 marks]

3 The graph of the curve $y = x^2 - x - 4$ is shown. Use the graph to estimate the solutions to $x^2 + x = 1$.

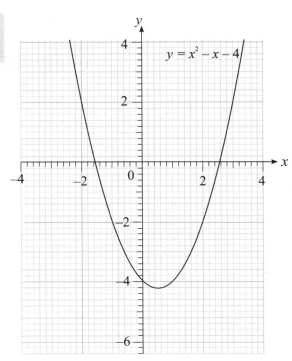

$y = x^2 - x - 4$

$x = $ ....

$x = $ ....

[Total 4 marks]

4 Find the equation of the tangent to the circle $x^2 + y^2 = 25$ at the point $(-4, -3)$.

Start by finding the equation of the radius that goes from (O, O) to (−4, −3).

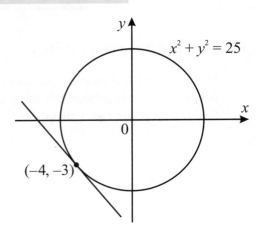

[Total 3 marks]

5 The diagram shows the curves $y = ab^x$ and $y = a(2b)^x$, where a and b are constants. The curve $y = ab^x$ passes through the points $A(2, 36)$ and $B(4, 81)$. The curve $y = a(2b)^x$ passes through the points C and D. C and D lie vertically above A and B.

Calculate the gradient of the line segment CD.

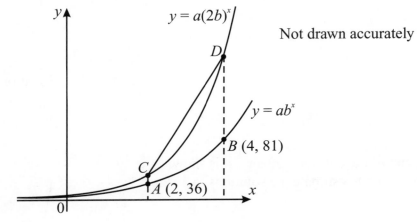

Not drawn accurately

[Total 5 marks]

Score:

17

Section Three — Graphs

Trig Graphs

1   The graph of $y = -\cos x$ is shown below for $0° \leq x \leq 360°$.

As shown on the graph,
$-\cos 75° = -0.259$.

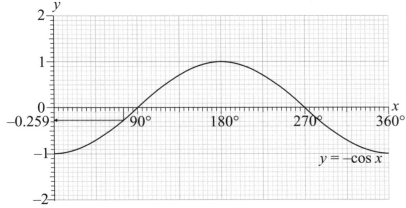

Give another value of x, found on this graph, where $-\cos x = -0.259$.

$x = \text{.........................}°$

[Total 1 mark]

2   The diagram shows a sketch of $y = \tan x$ for $0° \leq x \leq 360°$.

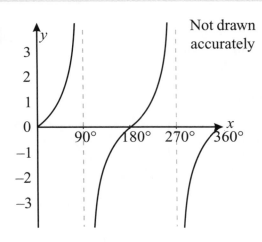

Not drawn accurately

$\tan 105° = -3.732$.

Write down the two solutions to the equation $\tan x = 3.732$ for $0° \leq x \leq 360°$.

$x = \text{.........................}°$ and $x = \text{.........................}°$

[Total 2 marks]

3   The graphs of $y = \sin x$ and $y = \sin 2x$ for $0° \leq x \leq 360°$ are shown below.

For the graph of $y = \sin 2x + 3$, find the exact y-value when $x = 22.5°$

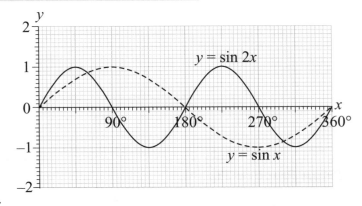

$y = \text{.........................}$

[Total 2 marks]

4   The diagram shows a sketch of $y = \cos x$ for $0° \le x \le 180°$.

As shown on the graph, $\cos 55° = 0.574$.

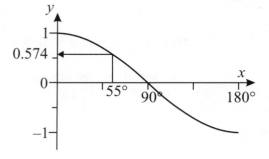

 a) Find the value of x in the range $0° \le x \le 180°$
for which $\cos x = -0.574$.

$x =$ ....°

[1]

b) Find the value of x in the range $180° \le x \le 360°$ for which $\cos x = -0.574$.

$x =$ ....°

[1]

c) Find the value of x in the range $-180° \le x \le 0°$ for which $\cos x = 0.574$.

$x =$ ....°

[1]

[Total 3 marks]

5   The sketch below shows the graphs of $y = \tan x$ and $y = -\sin x + c$,
where c is a positive number. The two graphs intersect when $x = 45°$.

 The point $(90°, a)$ lies on the curve $y = -\sin x + c$.
Work out the exact value of a.

Remember the common
trig values — they'll come
in handy for this question.

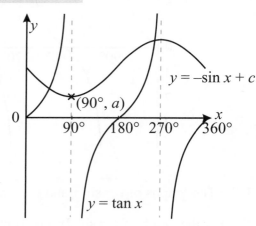

$y = -\sin x + c$

$(90°, a)$

$y = \tan x$

Not drawn accurately

$a =$ ....

[Total 4 marks]

Exam Practice Tip

It's really, really important that you know all the properties of the sin, cos and tan graphs — their shapes,
where they cross the x- and y-axes, any symmetry they have, where the pattern repeats etc. If you're not given
the graph over a big enough range to solve the question, you can always draw a quick sketch to help you.

Score

12

Graph Transformations

1   For parts a) and b) below, draw the transformed graphs on the same axes as the original graphs.

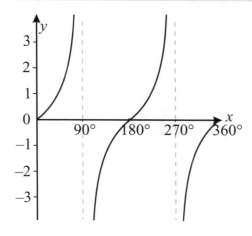

a) The graph on the left shows a sketch of $y = \tan x$
   for $0° \leq x \leq 360°$. Sketch the graph of $y = -\tan x$.

[1]

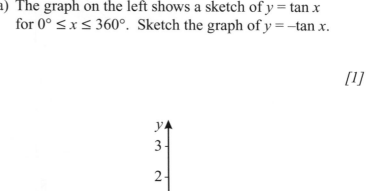

b) The graph on the right shows a sketch of $y = \sin x$
   for $0° \leq x \leq 360°$. Sketch the graph of $y = \sin x + 2$.

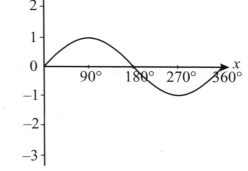

[1]

[Total 2 marks]

2   The diagram shows a sketch of $y = f(x)$, which crosses the x-axis at -4 and 1,
     and has a turning point at $(-3, 4)$.

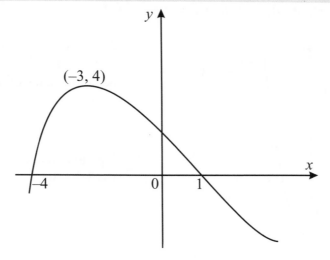

a) On the same axes, sketch the graph of $y = f(-x)$, labelling the turning point
   and where it crosses the x-axis.

[3]

b) Write down the coordinates of the turning point of $y = f(x + 3) + 2$.

(..................... , ...)

[2]

[Total 5 marks]

Section Three — Graphs

3   The circle $x^2 + y^2 = 36$ is shown below.

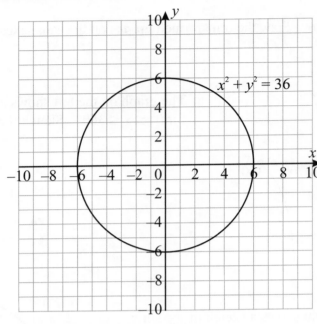

a) On the same axes, sketch the graph of $(x - 2)^2 + y^2 = 36$.

Don't be put off by the fact that the equation isn't in the form $y = f(x)$ — you can use the transformation rules in the same way.

[2]

b) Write down the coordinates of the centre of the graph $(x + 6)^2 + y^2 = 36$.

(..................... , ...)

[1]

[Total 3 marks]

4   The diagram below shows the graph of $y = x^3 + 3x^2 + 2$.

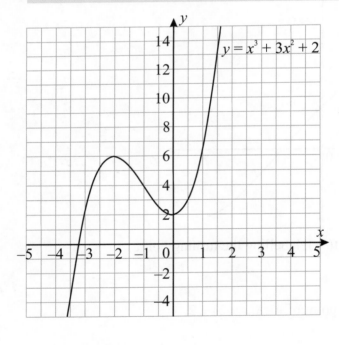

a) On the same axes, draw the graph of $y = (x - 3)^3 + 3(x - 3)^2 + 1$, showing clearly the coordinates of any turning points.

[3]

b) Expand and simplify $(x - 3)^3 + 3(x - 3)^2 + 1$.

....

[4]

[Total 7 marks]

5   The diagram shows a sketch of $y = f(x)$, where $f(x) = x^2 - 5x + 7$.

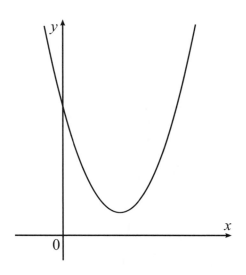

a) By completing the square, find the coordinates
of the turning point of f(x).

(................... , ...)

[3]

b) Hence find the coordinates of the turning point of
$y = f(x + 3) - 2$.

(................... , ...)

[2]

c) Find the x-values of the points where the graph of $y = f(x + 3) - 2$ intersects the x-axis.

$x =$ .... and $x =$ ....

[3]

[Total 8 marks]

6   The graph $y = \dfrac{6}{x}$ is transformed into the graph of $y = \dfrac{3x}{x - 2}$.

a) Show that $\dfrac{ab}{x - a} + b \equiv \dfrac{bx}{x - a}$.

[2]

b) Describe the transformation that maps the graph of $y = \dfrac{6}{x}$ to the graph of $y = \dfrac{3x}{x - 2}$.

....

....

Start by using the identity in part a) to
rewrite the second equation in part b).

[3]

[Total 5 marks]

Score: ⬚

30

Velocity-Time Graphs

1   Estimate the distance covered by the tractor whose
     journey is shown on the velocity-time graph below.

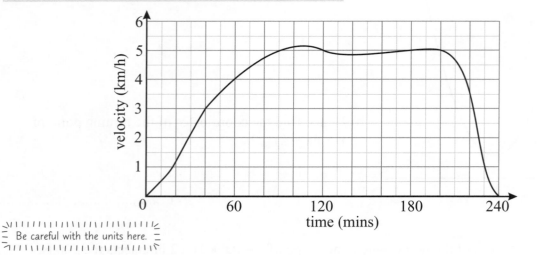

Be careful with the units here.

.... km

[Total 3 marks]

2   This velocity-time graph models the first 150 seconds of a journey.

a) Calculate an estimate for the
   distance travelled during these
   150 seconds.

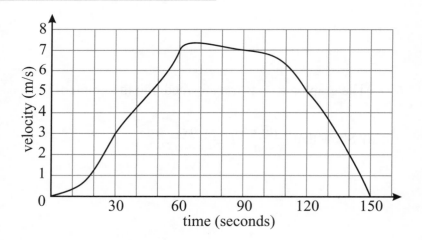

.... m

[3]

b) Is your answer to part a) an underestimate or an overestimate? Give a reason for your answer.

     ....

     ....

[2]

[Total 5 marks]

3   A go-kart's velocity over one lap is plotted on the velocity-time graph below.

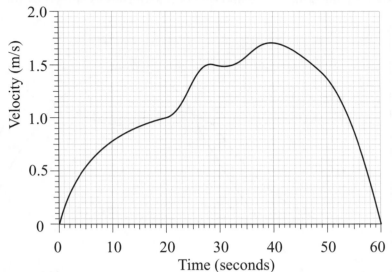

Calculate an estimate for its average speed.

You'll need to find the total distance the go-kart travelled first.

.... m/s

[Total 4 marks]

4   The velocity-time graph below shows the journey of a hot-air balloon.

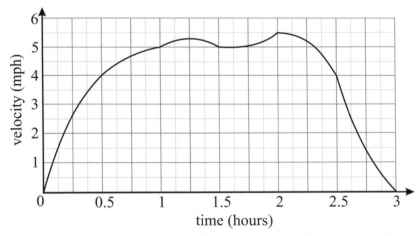

Find the percentage decrease between the estimates for the total distance travelled when the area is split into six strips and into three strips of equal width. Give your answer to 1 decimal place.

.... %

[Total 6 marks]

Section Three — Graphs

5 The velocity-time graph below shows the journeys of two different objects, *A* and *B*. Object *A*'s journey is shown by the solid curve and object *B*'s journey is shown by the dashed curve.

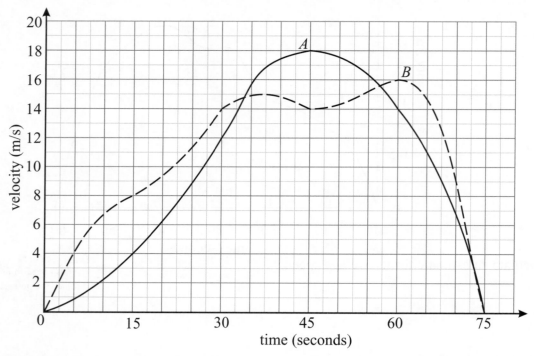

By dividing each area into 5 strips of equal width, calculate the ratio of the estimated average speed of object *A* to the estimated average speed of object *B*. Give your answer in its simplest form.

....

[Total 6 marks]

Exam Practice Tip

Finding the area under velocity-time graphs is much harder if the graphs are curved, not straight. You can't find the exact area, only an estimate by dividing it up into triangles, rectangles and trapeziums. Remember, the gradient of the line shows the acceleration — and a negative gradient means the object is slowing down.

Score

24

Gradients

1 The temperature of an indoor swimming pool is recorded and shown on the graph below.

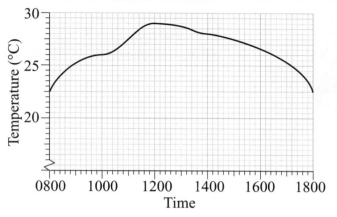

The manager claims that the average rate of change of the temperature between 8 am and 12 noon is the same as the average rate of change of the temperature between 4 pm and 6 pm.

Is the manager correct? Explain your answer.

....

....

....

....

[Total 3 marks]

2 The first 60 seconds of a cyclist's journey are shown on the velocity-time graph below.

a) Find the average acceleration of the cyclist between 10 and 20 seconds.

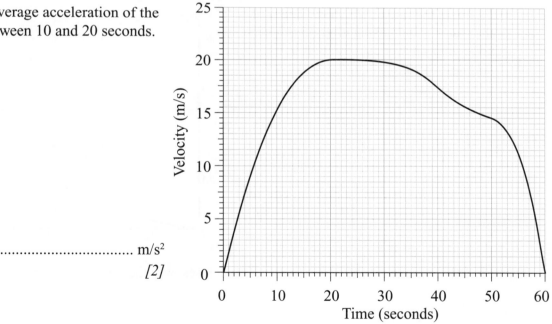

.... m/s²

[2]

b) Estimate the acceleration of the cyclist at 50 seconds. Give your answer to 3 s.f.

Draw a tangent to the curve at 50 seconds.

.... m/s²

[2]

[Total 4 marks]

Section Three — Graphs

46

3 A scientist measures the growth of two different plants over two weeks.
Her results are shown in the graph below.

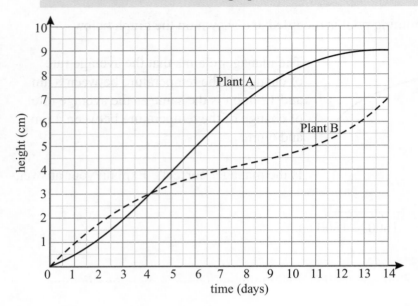

Find an estimate of the ratio of the rate of growth of plant A during the first week to the rate of growth of plant B during the second week.
Give your answer in its simplest form.

....

[Total 3 marks]

4 The graph shows the depth of water in a container.

a) Estimate the rate at which the depth of the water is increasing after 35 minutes. Give your answer as a fraction in its simplest form.

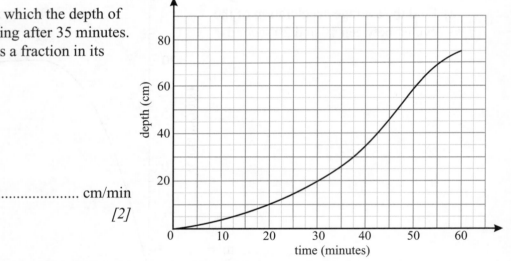

.... cm/min
[2]

b) Find the average rate at which the water increases over the 60 minute period.

.... cm/min
[2]

[Total 4 marks]

Score:

14

Section Three — Graphs

Ratios

1   A rowing boat travelled 18 km in 2 hours 15 minutes.
A canoe travelled 15 miles in 1 hour 30 minutes.

   What is the approximate ratio of the speed of the rowing boat to the speed of the canoe?
Give your answer in its simplest form.

....

[Total 4 marks]

2   Abbey draws two triangles, A and B.
The height of triangle B is 1 cm more than the height of triangle A.
The bases of triangle A and triangle B are in the ratio $1:3$.
The areas of triangle A and triangle B are in the ratio $2:9$. Triangle B has an area of 45 cm².

   What is the ratio of the vertical height of triangle A to the vertical height of triangle B?

....

[Total 5 marks]

3   Jenna and Harvey both play a computer game.
The percentages of the game Jenna and Harvey have completed are in the ratio $3:4$.
If they were both to complete another 7% of the game, the ratio would become $7:9$.

What percentage of the game has Jenna completed?

.... %

[Total 4 marks]

4 At a school there are x Year 8 pupils and y Year 9 pupils.
If 10 pupils from each year group left the school, the ratio of pupils in Year 8 to Year 9 would be $2:5$. If 8 pupils were added to each year group, the ratio would be $1:2$.

Express x as a percentage of y.

.... %

[Total 5 marks]

5 A bag contains sweets that are either red, yellow or green.
The bag contains equal numbers of red and green sweets.

Luke eats 5 red, 15 yellow and 25 green sweets from the bag.
The ratio of red to yellow sweets remaining in the bag is $2:3$
The ratio of yellow to green sweets remaining in the bag is $3:1$

What fraction of the sweets originally in the bag were yellow?
Give your answer in its simplest form.

....

[Total 6 marks]

Score:

24

Direct and Inverse Proportion

1 If you hang an object on the end of a spring, the amount that the spring stretches by, x cm, is directly proportional to the mass of the object, M g. When $M = 40$, $x = 2$.

a) Write an equation connecting x and M.

....
[3]

b) How much would the spring stretch if an object with a mass of 55 g was hung on the end of it?

.... cm
[1]
[Total 4 marks]

2 The weight, w g, of a sphere is directly proportional to the cube of its radius, r cm.

a) When the radius is 6 cm, the sphere weighs 1080 g.
What is the radius of a sphere weighing 8.64 kg?

.... cm
[4]

b) Sketch the graph of w against r on the axes on the right.

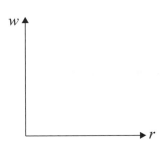

[1]
[Total 5 marks]

3 p is directly proportional to q and q is inversely proportional to r.

When $p = 8$, $q = 25$ and $r = 16$. Find the value of p when $r = 2$.

$p =$ ....
[Total 5 marks]

50

4   *a* is inversely proportional to *b*.
     a is inversely proportional to c^2.

        Show that *b* is directly proportional to c^2.

[Total 3 marks]

5   The density of an object, *d* g/cm³, is inversely proportional to its volume, *v* cm³.

If the volume of the object is increased by 40%, what is the percentage decrease in its density?
Give your answer to 1 decimal place.

> Start by setting up equations for the densities of the object before and after the increase in volume.

.... %
[Total 4 marks]

6   *y* varies inversely with the square of *x*, as shown in the diagram on the right. *y* is also proportional to the cube of *z*.

When *x* = 2, *z* = 5. Calculate *y* when *z* = 15.

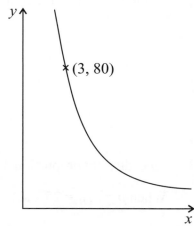

....
[Total 5 marks]

Score:
26

Section Four — Ratio, Proportion and Rates of Change

Percentages

1   In the first quarter of the year a company's sales were £12 million. In each of the next three quarters, sales were 10% higher than the previous quarter. 28% of the company's sales are profit. At the end of the year 30% of the company profits are given to the employees as a bonus.

How much was given to the employees as a bonus?
Give your answer to 2 significant figures.

There are 4 quarters in a year.

£ ....
[Total 4 marks]

2   Simone took 3 maths exams. She scored 85% on exam A, which was out of 120 marks and 50% on exam B, which was out of 80 marks. On exam C she scored 95%.

She scored 75% of the total marks across the 3 exams. How many marks was exam C out of?

.... marks
[Total 4 marks]

3   Two cubes, *A* and *B*, have the same weight. Both are resting on horizontal ground. The side length of cube *B* is 20% longer than the side length of cube *A*.

Give the pressure that cube *A* exerts as a percentage of the pressure that cube *B* exerts.

.... %
[Total 4 marks]

Section Four — Ratio, Proportion and Rates of Change

4 An investment company guarantees 10% interest on a customer's investment per annum. At the end of each year the company takes any money above the 10% interest as a payment and reinvests the rest of the customer's money.

One customer's 3-year investment of £100 000 makes 12% interest per annum.
How much does the company make over the 3 years from this customer's investment?

£ ....

[Total 5 marks]

5 The pie charts show the types of houses in two villages.

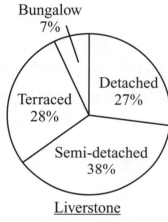

Liverstone

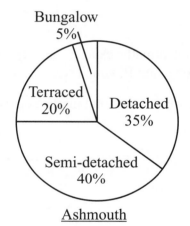

Ashmouth

There are 480 more terraced houses in Ashmouth than in Liverstone.
Ashmouth has 70% more houses in total than Liverstone.

Calculate how many more semi-detached houses there are in Ashmouth than in Liverstone.

Start by writing the number of houses in Ashmouth in terms of the number of houses in Liverstone (L).

....

[Total 5 marks]

Score: ☐

22

Section Four — Ratio, Proportion and Rates of Change

 ☐ ☐ ☐

Circle Geometry

1   The diagram shows triangle *ABC*, where *A*, *B* and *C* are points on the
circumference of a circle. *AB = AC*, and *DE* is a tangent to the circle at *C*.

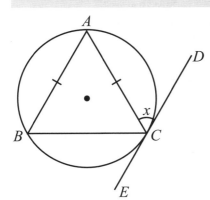

Angle *DCA = x*. *DE* is parallel to *AB*.
Prove that *ABC* is an equilateral triangle.
Give geometrical reasons to support the statements you make.

[Total 4 marks]

2   The diagram below shows the circle with centre *O*.
A, *B*, *C* and *D* are points on the circumference of the circle.

Find the size of angle *CDO*.

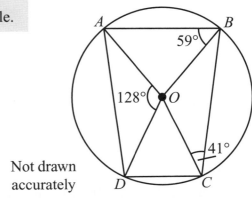

Not drawn
accurately

CDO = ...°
[Total 4 marks]

3   Prove that the angle formed at the circumference when
a triangle is drawn from both ends of a diameter is 90°.

Start by splitting the triangle
into two isosceles triangles.

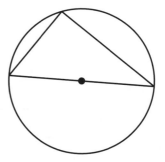

[Total 3 marks]

4 The diagram below shows two intersecting circles with centres *O* and *P*. The circles intersect at *C* and *E*. *A*, *B* and *F* are points on the circumference with centre *O*, and *D* is a point on the circumference of the circle with centre *P*. *BD* and *DF* are straight lines.

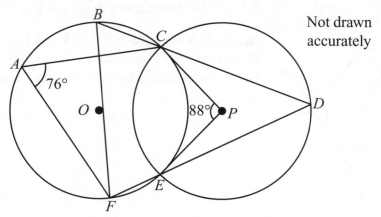

Not drawn accurately

Find the size of angle *BFE*. Give reasons for each step of your working.

BFE = ...°

[Total 3 marks]

5 Points *A*, *B*, *C* and *D* are points on the circumference of the circle below. *EF* is a tangent that meets the circle at *D*, and *AC* and *BD* are straight lines.

Show that *X* is NOT the centre of the circle.

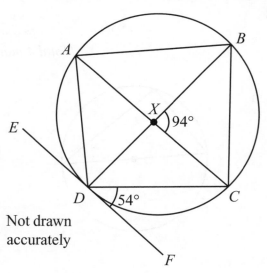

Not drawn accurately

[Total 4 marks]

Section Five — Geometry and Measures

6   The diagram shows a circle with centre *O*. *B*, *C*, *E* and *F* are points on the circumference of the circle. *AB* and *AF* are tangents to the circle, and *BD* and *DF* are straight lines.

Find the size of angle *CDE*.

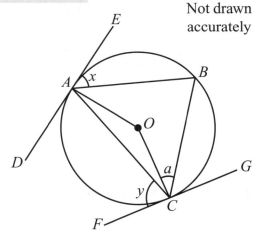

B

56°

C

112°

A

36°

O

D

E

F

Not drawn accurately

$CDE =$ ....$^{\circ}$

[Total 5 marks]

7   The diagram shows a circle with centre *O*.
DE is a tangent to the circle at *A* and *FG* is a tangent to the circle at *C*.

Prove that $a = x + y - 90°$.
State any circle theorems that you use.

Not drawn accurately

E

A   x

B

O

D

a   G

y

C

F

[Total 4 marks]

Exam Practice Tip

It's not always easy to spot which circle theorems you need to use — so just go through them one by one until you find one that works. There are usually one or two you can discount straight away (for example, if there are no tangents on the diagram, you probably aren't going to need the theorems that involve tangents).

Score

27

Similarity and Congruence

1   The diagram below shows parallelogram *ABCF*. *AFE* is a straight line.

Prove that triangles *BCD* and *ABE* are similar.

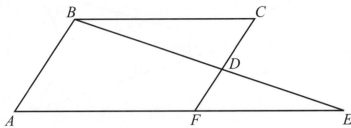

[Total 3 marks]

2   Points *A*, *B*, *C* and *D* are points on the circumference
of the circle below, and *ABCD* is an isosceles trapezium.

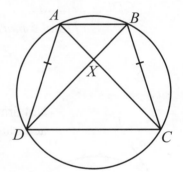

Prove that triangles *AXD* and *BXC* are congruent.

[Total 3 marks]

3   *ABC* is a right-angled triangle.

a) Construct a line that is perpendicular to *AC*
   and passes through point *B*. Label the point
   where the line crosses side *AC* point *D*.

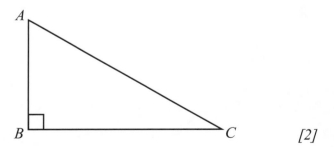

[2]

b) Show that triangles *ABD* and *BCD* are similar.

[3]

[Total 5 marks]

Section Five — Geometry and Measures

4 *ABCD* is a parallelogram. *M, N, P* and *Q* are the midpoints of *AB, BC, CD* and *DA* respectively. *R* is the midpoint of *MQ, S* is the midpoint of *BD* and *T* is the midpoint of *NP*.

Prove that triangles *AMQ* and *NCP* are congruent.

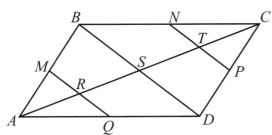

[Total 4 marks]

5 Lines L_1 and L_2 are perpendicular, and line L_3 is a vertical line. Lines L_1 and L_2 intersect at point *P*, which has coordinates (2, 2.5). Lines L_2 and L_3 intersect at point *R*, which lies on the *x*-axis. The equation of line L_2 is $5x + 4y = 20$.

Prove that triangles *MNP* and *QRP* are congruent.

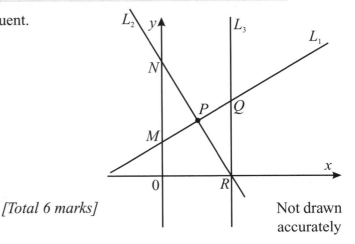

[Total 6 marks]

Not drawn accurately

6 The diagram shows a circle with centre *O*. *AB* is a chord, and the radius *OP* is perpendicular to *AB*.

Prove that *OP* bisects the chord *AB*.

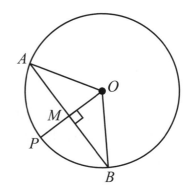

[Total 4 marks]

Exam Practice Tip

Remember the four conditions for congruence — SSS, AAS, SAS and RHS. Then all you have to do is find any side lengths and angles that you can, and see which condition they fit. Don't forget to state the condition at the end of your answer — e.g. 'the condition SSS holds, so the triangles are congruent'.

Score

25

Arcs, Sectors and Segments

1   The major sector on the right has an area of 88π cm^2.

Find the size of angle x.

Not drawn accurately

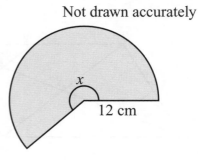

12 cm

$x = $ ....°

[Total 3 marks]

2   The diagram on the right shows a sector of a circle.

a) Find the area of the shaded segment. Give your answer to 3 s.f.

Not drawn accurately

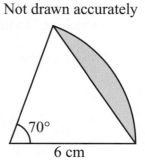

70°

6 cm

.... cm^2

[3]

b) Find the perimeter of the shaded segment. Give your answer to 3 s.f.

You need to use the
cosine rule for part b).

.... cm

[4]

[Total 7 marks]

3   A circle of radius 8 cm is divided up into equal sectors.
The perimeter of each sector is 21.6 cm to 3 s.f.

How many sectors are there in total?

....

[Total 3 marks]

Section Five — Geometry and Measures

4 Hannah cuts a slice of cake. The cake has a radius of 10 cm, and Hannah's slice is a sector with angle 45°. The cake is covered in two different colours of icing, as shown below.

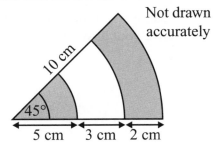

a) Find the area of white icing on Hannah's slice of cake.
Give your answer to 3 s.f.

.... cm²
[3]

b) The height of the cake is 8 cm. Find the volume of Hannah's slice.
Give your answer to 3 s.f.

.... cm³
[2]

[Total 5 marks]

5 The diagram shows sector *ABC* of a circle with centre *C* and sector *DEF* of a circle with centre *F*. The diagram has a vertical line of symmetry, and *D* is the midpoint of *AC*.

DF = 1.6 cm, angle *DFE* = 140° and angle *DCE* = 60°.

a) By considering triangle *DFC*, calculate the length of *DC*.
Give your answer to 3 s.f.

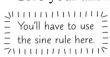

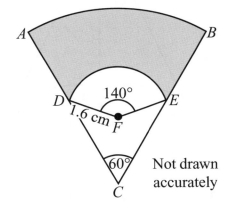

.... cm
[3]

b) Calculate the perimeter of the shaded region *ADEB*. Give your answer to 3 s.f.

.... cm
[5]

[Total 8 marks]

Score:

26

Section Five — Geometry and Measures

3D Shapes — Surface Area and Volume

1 Find the volume of the triangular prism below.
Give your answer to 3 significant figures.

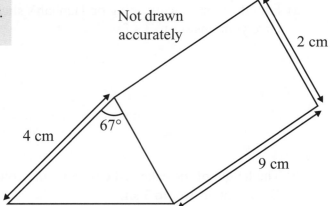

Not drawn accurately

2 cm

4 cm

67°

9 cm

.... cm³

[Total 3 marks]

2 The cone below has a volume of $(3.2 \times 10^{26})\pi$ m³ and a radius of 4×10^8 m.
Find x, the vertical height of the cone. Give your answer in standard form.

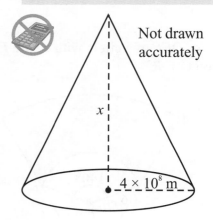

Not drawn accurately

x

4×10^8 m

The formula for the volume of a cone is $V = \frac{1}{3} \times \pi r^2 \times h_v$.

.... m

[Total 3 marks]

3 Sphere A has radius 6 cm. The volume of sphere B is 60% greater
than the volume of sphere A. What is the radius of sphere B?

Give your answer to 3 significant figures.

The formula for the volume of a sphere is $V = \frac{4}{3}\pi r^3$.

.... cm

[Total 4 marks]

4 A cone has radius 15 cm and height 36 cm. The top of the cone is removed to create a frustum two-thirds of the height of the original cone.

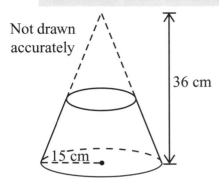

Not drawn accurately

36 cm

15 cm

a) Find the exact volume of the frustum.

.... cm³
[3]

b) Find the exact surface area of the frustum.

.... cm²
[3]

[Total 6 marks]

5 A piece of apparatus for an experiment is made up of a cone within a cylinder. The cone and cylinder have the same radius, and the vertical height of the cone is the same as the vertical height of the cylinder (as shown in the diagram).

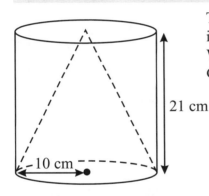

21 cm

10 cm

Not drawn accurately

The space within the cylinder not taken up by the cone is filled with a gas. The gas has a density of 0.52 kg/m³. What is the mass of the gas in the cylinder? Give your answer in grams to 3 significant figures.

Be careful with the units here.

.... g
[Total 6 marks]

6 A cone and a cylinder have the same radius, *r*. The slant height of the cone is 7 cm and the height of the cylinder is 6 cm. The combined surface area of both shapes is 110π cm².

Find the radius, *r*, of the cone and the cylinder.

r = ... cm
[Total 6 marks]

Section Five — Geometry and Measures

7   A sphere with radius 1.4 m is cut into 8 identical pieces, as shown below. The weight of the whole sphere is 5000 N.

One piece of the sphere is resting on horizontal ground on one of the flat faces.
Find the pressure exerted on the ground. Give your answer to 3 significant figures.

1.4 m

.... N/m²

[Total 4 marks]

8   The diagram shows a solid object made up of a hemisphere of radius $3k$ cm and a cone with vertical height $4k$ cm. The total surface area of the object is 3993π cm².

Work out the value of k.

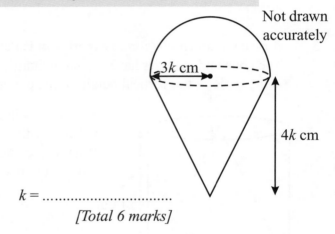

Not drawn accurately

$3k$ cm

$4k$ cm

$k =$ ....

[Total 6 marks]

9   Josie melts down 1200 cm³ of steel. She uses 30% of the steel to make two identical spheres.
She uses $\frac{1}{3}$ of the steel to make four identical cones with the same radius as the spheres.

Work out whether Josie has enough steel left to make one cube
with side length equal to the height of the cone.

[Total 6 marks]

Score:

44

Section Five — Geometry and Measures

Rates of Flow

1 The cylindrical tank below is full of water. The plug is removed, and the tank empties.
It takes 25 minutes before the tank is completely empty.

Find the rate of flow of the water. Give your answer in litres per minute to 3 significant figures.

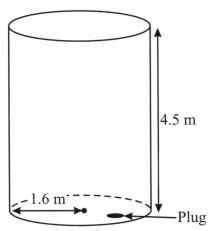

Not drawn accurately

.... litres/min

[Total 4 marks]

2 The bottom half of an egg-timer is the shape of the cone below.
The circular base is resting on a flat horizontal surface.
Liquid flows from the top half of the timer into the bottom half at a rate of 0.5 cm³/s.

When the timer is started, the cone is empty.
a) How long does it take for the liquid in the bottom half of the timer
to reach a depth of 2 cm? Give your answer in seconds to 3 s.f.

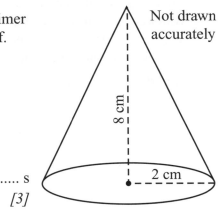

Not drawn accurately

.... s

[3]

b) When the timer has finished, liquid has filled 89.5% (by volume) of the
bottom half of the egg-timer to 3 s.f. How long does the timer last for?

.... s

[2]

[Total 5 marks]

Section Five — Geometry and Measures

64

3 A flood channel is built to divert excess water from a river.
The flood channel is the shape of a triangular prism.

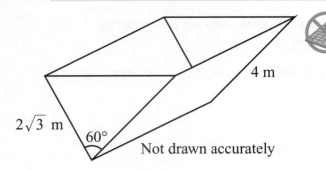

4 m

$2\sqrt{3}$ m

60°

Not drawn accurately

a) Find the exact cross-sectional area
of the flood channel.

.... m²

[2]

b) At the peak of a flood, the flood channel is full of water, which flows
at a rate of 90 000 litres per minute. Find the speed of the water in m/s.

.... m/s

[4]

[Total 6 marks]

4 A container is in the shape of a cylinder placed on top of a cone. The radius of each shape
is 30 cm, the height of the cylinder is 60 cm and the vertical height of the cone is 70 cm.

The container is filled at a rate of $x\pi$ litres per second.
Once it is full, the container is then emptied.
Water empties from the container at a
rate of $(x-2)\pi$ litres per second.
It takes 2 minutes longer to empty than it takes to fill.

Find the value of x.

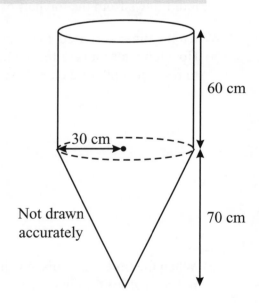

60 cm

30 cm

70 cm

Not drawn
accurately

$x = $ ....

[Total 7 marks]

Score:

22

Section Five — Geometry and Measures

Enlargement

1 Three cylinders are mathematically similar. Their radii are in the ratio $1:3:5$.
The smallest cylinder has a vertical height of 6 cm.

a) Write down the ratio of the surface areas of the three cylinders.

....
[1]

b) The volume of the largest cylinder is 6750π cm^3.
Find the radius of the middle cylinder.

.... cm
[3]

[Total 4 marks]

2 An Egyptian pyramid has a volume of 2.5×10^6 m^3.
A museum is building a scale model of the pyramid.

a) The model has a volume of 160 m^3.
Find the scale factor used for the model.
Give your answer as a fraction in its simplest form.

> The model is smaller than the original pyramid, so the scale factor will be less than 1.

....
[2]

b) The surface area of the model is 200 m^2.
What is the surface area of the original pyramid? Give your answer in standard form.

.... m^2
[2]

[Total 4 marks]

Section Five — Geometry and Measures

66

3 Two cones are mathematically similar. Cone A has a volume of 324π cm³ and cone B has a volume of 768π cm³. The surface area of cone A is 216π cm².

a) Find the exact surface area of cone B.

.... cm²
[2]

b) Write down the ratio of the radius of cone A to the radius of cone B.
Give your answer in its simplest form.

....
[1]

[Total 3 marks]

4 Cuboids A and B below are similar, and cuboid A has dimensions as shown.
The scale factor of enlargement from A to B is $\frac{8}{5}$.

1.5 cm   A   5 cm
   2.5 cm

B

Not drawn accurately

a) Find the volume of cuboid B.

.... cm³
[2]

b) The cuboids are made out of different types of metal and both have a mass of 0.06 kg.
Find the percentage decrease in density from cuboid A to cuboid B.
Give your answer to 3 significant figures.

.... %
[3]

[Total 5 marks]

5   Will buys a set of three vases. The vases are mathematically similar and have bases with areas of 90 cm², 160 cm² and 1440 cm². The volume of the largest vase is 0.016 m³ and the height of the medium vase is 20 cm.

Find the height and volume of the smallest vase.

height = ... cm

volume = ... cm³

[Total 4 marks]

6   Anna makes necklaces using spherical beads. She has two different sizes of beads. Small beads have a volume of 2.4 cm³ and large beads have a volume of 8.1 cm³.

The time taken to decorate a bead is proportional to the surface area of the bead.
It takes 8 minutes to decorate a small bead.
She uses 5 small beads and 4 large beads to make a necklace.

Can she decorate all the beads needed for a necklace in $1\frac{3}{4}$ hours?
Show how you worked out your answer.

[Total 4 marks]

Exam Practice Tip

Just remember — for a scale factor of n, side lengths are n times bigger, areas (or surface areas) are n² times bigger and volumes are n³ times bigger. If you have a fractional scale factor, don't forget to square and cube both the numerator and denominator of the fraction to find the area and volume of the enlarged shape.

Score

24

Trigonometry

1   Triangles P and Q are shown below.

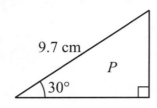

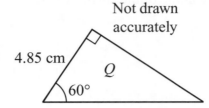

Not drawn accurately

9.7 cm P 30°

4.85 cm Q 60°

Prove that triangle P is congruent to triangle Q.

[Total 4 marks]

2   The diagram below shows a large rhombus made up from four smaller rhombuses.

Show that the area of the large rhombus is $4n^2\sin\theta$ cm^2.

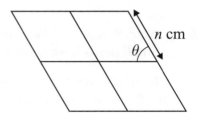

n cm

θ

[Total 3 marks]

3   The diagram on the right shows a kite *EFGH*.
Diagonal *EG* bisects the diagonal *HF* at *M*.
EM = 5 cm and *MG* = 9 cm.

Calculate the size of angle *FEH*.
Give your answer to 1 decimal place.

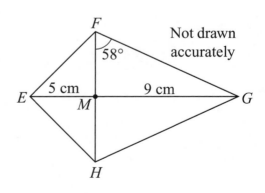

Not drawn accurately

F 58°

E 5 cm M 9 cm G

H

.........................°

[Total 3 marks]

4   The diagram shows two right-angled triangles, *ABC* and *BCD*, and a semicircle.

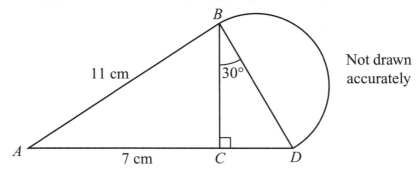

Not drawn
accurately

AB = 11 cm, *AC* = 7 cm and angle *CBD* = 30°.
Calculate the exact area of the semicircle.

.... cm²

[Total 5 marks]

5   *A*, *B*, *C* and *D* are points on a circle. *EF* is a tangent to the circle at *C*.

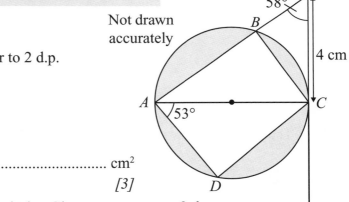

AC is a diameter of the circle. *EC* = 4 cm.
Angle *BEC* = 58° and angle *DAC* = 53°.
a) Find the area of the circle. Give your answer to 2 d.p.

Not drawn
accurately

.... cm²
[3]

b) Find the total area of the shaded parts of the circle. Give your answer to 2 d.p.

.... cm²
[5]

[Total 8 marks]

Score:

23

Section Six — Pythagoras and Trigonometry

The Sine and Cosine Rules

1   The diagram shows triangle *ABC*.

$AB = \sqrt{6}$ cm, $BC = 4\sqrt{2}$ cm and $AC = \sqrt{14}$ cm.
Show that $x = 30°$.

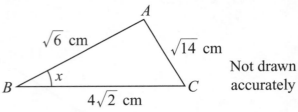

[Total 4 marks]

2   The diagram on the right is a sketch of a metal framework.
Some of the information needed to manufacture the framework has been lost.

Complete the specification for the framework
by calculating the size of angle *BDC*.
Give your answer to 3 significant figures.

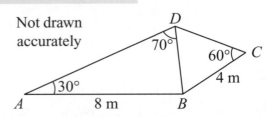

..........................°

[Total 5 marks]

3   The diagram below shows two triangles, *ABC* and *DEF*.

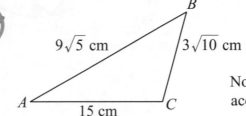

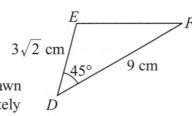

Show that triangle *ABC* and triangle *DEF* are similar.

[Total 4 marks]

Section Six — Pythagoras and Trigonometry

4 Points *A*, *B*, *C* and *D* are points on the circumference of a circle with centre *O*. *DC* = 18 cm, angle *DOC* = 74° and angle *AOB* = 26°.

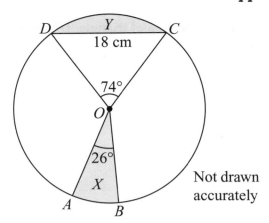

Not drawn accurately

Work out which shaded area, *X* or *Y*, is bigger.
Show your working.

....

[Total 6 marks]

5 *ABCDE* is an irregular pentagon.

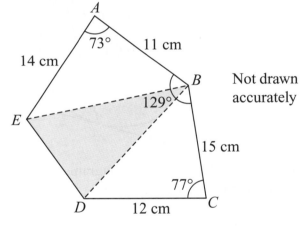

Not drawn accurately

What is the area of triangle *BED*? Give your answer to 3 significant figures.

.... cm²

[Total 5 marks]

Section Six — Pythagoras and Trigonometry

72

6 The area of triangle *ABC* is 38 cm².

AB : *BC* = 1 : 2. Angle *ABC* = 50°.
Find *AC*, giving your answer to 3 significant figures.

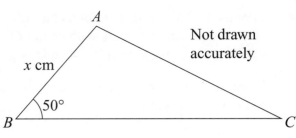

.... cm

[Total 4 marks]

7 *A* and *B* are points on a circle with centre *O*.
CD is a tangent to the circle at *A* and *CE* is a tangent to the circle at *B*.

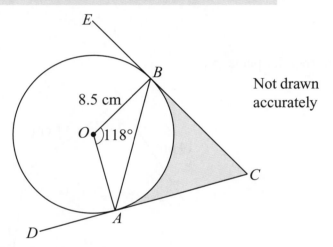

Calculate the area of the shaded part of the diagram.
Give your answer to 3 significant figures.

Find the area of the minor segment, then subtract it from the area of triangle ABC.

.... cm²

[Total 7 marks]

Score:

35

Section Six — Pythagoras and Trigonometry

3D Pythagoras and Trigonometry

1 The solid on the right is made from two identical cones joined at their bases. The slant height of each cone is 4.2 m and the overall vertical height of the solid is 6 m.

Work out the volume of the solid.
Give your answer to 3 significant figures.

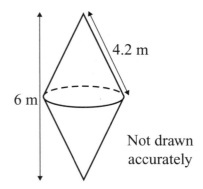

4.2 m

6 m

Not drawn accurately

.... m³
[Total 3 marks]

2 The triangular prism *ABCDEF* is shown on the right.

Angle *ACB* = 30°, *AC* = $2\sqrt{3}$ cm.
Area of rectangle *BCFE* = 32 cm².
Work out the exact volume of the prism.

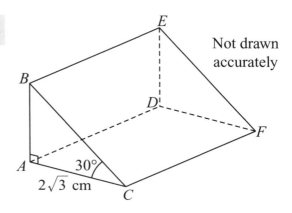

Not drawn accurately

$2\sqrt{3}$ cm

30°

.... cm³
[Total 4 marks]

3 The diagram shows a pyramid with a rectangular base. The vertex, *V*, of the pyramid is directly above the centre of the base *ABCD*.

VC = 8.9 cm, *VX* = 7.2 cm and *BC* = 4.2 cm.
Work out the length *AB*. Give your answer to 3 significant figures.

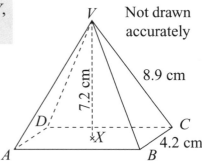

Not drawn accurately

7.2 cm

8.9 cm

4.2 cm

.... cm
[Total 4 marks]

4 The base of the pyramid *ABCDEFV* is a regular hexagon with side length 8 cm.
The vertex, *V*, of the pyramid is directly above the centre of the base, *X*.

The height *VX* of the pyramid is 15 cm.

Calculate the angle between the plane *VED* and
the base *ABCDEF*. Give your answer to 1 decimal place.

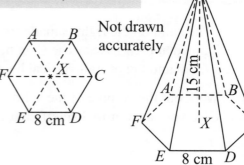

Not drawn
accurately

.... °

[Total 3 marks]

5 The diagram shows a prism *ABCDEFGH*.
ABFE is a square, and *M* and *N* are the midpoints of *DH* and *BF* respectively.

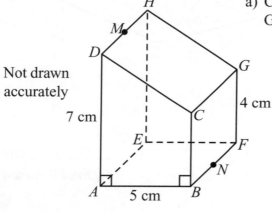

Not drawn
accurately

a) Calculate the angle between the line *HB* and the base *ABFE*.
Give your answer to 3 significant figures.

.... °

[3]

b) Calculate angle *BMF*. Give your answer to 3 significant figures.

.... °

[3]

[Total 6 marks]

Section Six — Pythagoras and Trigonometry

6 The diagram shows a prism *ABCDEFGH*.

Calculate the angle *DEG*.
Give your answer to 3 significant figures.

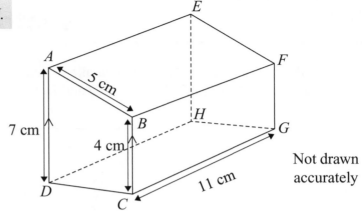

Not drawn accurately

...........................°

[Total 5 marks]

7 *ABCDEF* is a triangular prism.

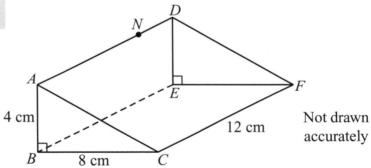

Not drawn accurately

A is vertically above *B* with *AB* = 4 cm. *BC* = 8 cm and *CF* = 12 cm.
N is the point on *AD* such that *AN* : *ND* = 3 : 1.

Calculate the angle *CNF*. Give your answer to 1 decimal place.

...........................°

[Total 5 marks]

Score:

30

Vectors

1 In the diagram below *ABCD* is a parallelogram.
The ratios *AE : EB, BF : FC, CG : GD* and *DH : HA* are all 2 : 1.

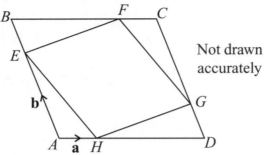

Not drawn
accurately

$\overrightarrow{AH}$ = **a** and $\overrightarrow{AE}$ = **b**. Show that *EFGH* is parallelogram.

[Total 3 marks]

2 *ABCD* is a parallelogram.

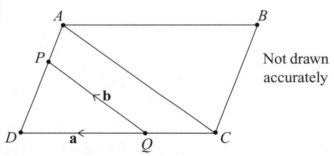

Not drawn
accurately

$\overrightarrow{QP}$ = **b** and $\overrightarrow{QD}$ = **a**. Triangles *PQD* and *ACD* are similar and *AD : PD* = 5 : 3

a) Find $\overrightarrow{CA}$ in terms of **a** and **b**.

....

[1]

R is a point on *AC* such that $5\overrightarrow{AR}$ = $2\overrightarrow{AC}$.

b) Given that $\overrightarrow{PR} = k\overrightarrow{DQ}$, find the value of *k*.

k = ...

[3]

[Total 4 marks]

3   *ABCD* is a parallelogram.

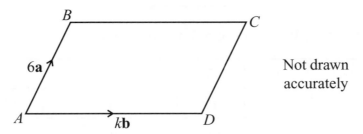

Not drawn accurately

$\overrightarrow{AB} = 6\mathbf{a}$ and $\overrightarrow{AD} = k\mathbf{b}$.

When the line *AC* is extended, *E* is a point on *AC* such that $\overrightarrow{BE} = 4\mathbf{a} + 25\mathbf{b}$.

Calculate the value of *k*.

$k =$ ....

[Total 4 marks]

4   The shape below is made up of two triangles, *ABF* and *BCF*, and a parallelogram *CDEF*.

$\overrightarrow{AB} = 3\mathbf{a}$ and $\overrightarrow{AF} = \frac{15}{4}\mathbf{a} + 2\mathbf{b}$.

ABCD is a straight line with $AB:BC:CD = 4:3:4$.

M is a point on *CF* such that $4\overrightarrow{FM} = \overrightarrow{MC}$.

Is *AME* a straight line? Explain your answer.

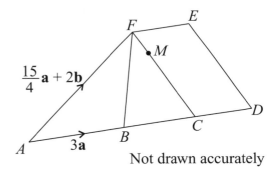

Not drawn accurately

[Total 5 marks]

Score:

16

Probability

1   The table below shows the results of rolling a dice 200 times.

Number	1	2	3	4	5	6
Frequency	54	12	38	9	61	26

a) What is the relative frequency of rolling an odd number? Give your answer as a decimal.

....

[2]

b) Desmond says, "If I roll the dice I am likely to get a 5." Criticise Desmond's statement.

....

....

[1]

[Total 3 marks]

2   Roger is looking at his serving statistics from a recent tennis match.
He served 150 points in total and on 70% of the points his first serve was in.
He won 80% of the points when his first serve was in
and he won 40% of the points when his first serve wasn't in.

a) Complete the frequency tree below to show this information.

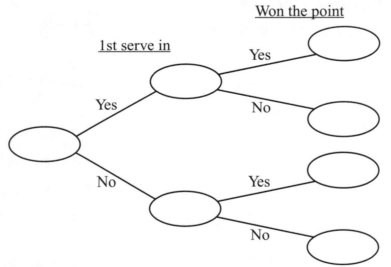

[3]

b) A sports TV channel randomly chooses one of the points that Roger served to analyse
on their highlights show. What is the probability that Roger won the chosen point?
Give your answer as a decimal.

....

[2]

[Total 5 marks]

3 An ice cream man states, "I sell over 5000 different combinations of ice cream". He has 16 different flavours of ice cream. You can either get 1, 2 or 3 scoops and you can combine different flavours. The ice cream man considers 'vanilla, chocolate' to be a different combination to 'chocolate, vanilla'.

Is the ice cream man's statement correct? Show working to support your answer.

....

....

....

[Total 3 marks]

4 Anya spins a spinner that has four sections numbered 1-4.
She is three times as likely to spin a 1 as to spin a 3.
She is twice as likely to spin an even number as an odd number.

a) What is the probability that she spins a 3?

....

[2]

b) What is the probability that, in two spins, she gets one even number and one odd number?

....

[2]

[Total 4 marks]

5 To break into a safe, Zane must find the correct 3-number combination (e.g. 17-6-11) for the combination lock shown on the right (numbered 1-20).

a) How many possible 3-number combinations are there for this lock?

....

[1]

Zane finds out that: • the first number is prime,
• the second number is odd,
• the third number is a square number.

b) What is the percentage decrease in the number of possible combinations?

....

[4]

[Total 5 marks]

Section Seven — Probability and Statistics

6 At a school, there are two Year 9 classes, A and B. Each class contains 30 students.
Mrs Dawson randomly selects one student from each class.
The probability that she selects a girl from class A (G_A) and a girl from class B (G_B) is 0.24.
The probability that she selects a girl from class A (G_A) and a boy from class B (B_B) is 0.56.

How many girls are there in Year 9?

> Form two simultaneous equations —
> remember that P(boy) = 1 − P(girl).

....

[Total 4 marks]

7 Jill has two bags containing blue and red balls.

Bag A	**Bag B**
14 blue	n blue
n red	30 red

When two blue balls are taken from Bag A and placed into Bag B,
the probability of picking a red ball is the same for both bags.

Show that the original probability of picking a red ball from Bag B is $\frac{5}{8}$.

[Total 6 marks]

Score:

30

Section Seven — Probability and Statistics

Tree Diagrams

1 A card is chosen at random from a standard pack of 52 cards.
It is then replaced and another card is chosen at random.

a) Complete the tree diagram below. Give probabilities as fractions in their simplest form.

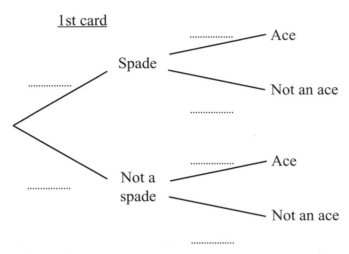

1st card

2nd card

.... — Ace

Spade

.... — Not an ace

....

....

.... — Ace

Not a
spade

.... — Not an ace

....

[2]

b) What is the probability that the first card is not a spade and the second card is not an ace?
Give your answer as a fraction in its simplest form.

....

[1]

[Total 3 marks]

2 A fair 12-sided dice numbered 1-12 is rolled three times.

a) What is the probability that all three rolls produce prime numbers?
Give your answer as a fraction in its simplest form.

....

[2]

b) What is the probability that exactly one of the numbers is less than 5?
Give your answer as a fraction in its simplest form.

....

[3]

[Total 5 marks]

Section Seven — Probability and Statistics

3   Mark is fishing for mackerel. He has 2 hooks on his line, so each time he casts his line he can catch either 0, 1 or 2 mackerel. On any cast, the probability that he catches 0 mackerel is 0.2, 1 mackerel is 0.5 and 2 mackerel is 0.3.

What is the probability that in 3 casts he catches less than 5 fish?

Hint: P(less than 5 fish) = 1 – P(5 or more fish).

....

[Total 4 marks]

4   A game at a fund-raising event involves throwing a dice twice and adding the scores together. The player wins a prize if the total is 11 or more.

a) It costs £2 to play the game and there are 20 prizes to be won.
Explain why the stall can expect to take about £480.

[3]

b) Pablo plays the game twice. Find the probability than he wins at least one prize.
Give your answer as a fraction.

....

[3]

[Total 6 marks]

Exam Practice Tip

Even when questions don't mention tree diagrams, it's often a good idea to draw one so that you don't make any silly mistakes. If you're feeling confident, you don't need to draw the whole diagram — just draw the branches that you think you'll need to be able to answer the question.

Score

18

Section Seven — Probability and Statistics

Conditional Probability

1   A biscuit barrel contains 8 chocolate biscuits and 6 plain biscuits.
Graham selects two biscuits at random without replacement.

What is the probability that both biscuits are the same?

....
[Total 3 marks]

2   A shop has 12 tubs of ice cream left. Five of the tubs are chocolate (C), four of the tubs are vanilla
(V) and three of the tubs are strawberry (S). Two tubs are selected at random without replacement.

   a) Calculate the probability that one chocolate tub and one strawberry tub are chosen.
   Give your answer as a fraction in its simplest form.

....
[3]

   b) Work out the probability that at least one tub is vanilla.
   Give your answer as a fraction in its simplest form.

....
[3]
[Total 6 marks]

3   The probability that Martyn goes to aerobics any evening is 0.4. If he doesn't
go to aerobics, the probability that he goes for a run the next morning is 0.7.

What is the probability that he doesn't go to aerobics
and doesn't go for a run the next morning?

....
[Total 3 marks]

Section Seven — Probability and Statistics

4 In a tombola there are 100 tickets numbered 1-100.
You win a prize if you pick a ticket that ends in 0 or 5.

a) Amy is the first person to play and picks two tickets at random.
   What is the probability that she wins at least one prize?

....

[4]

b) Carla plays after 40 tickets have been chosen and 5 prizes have been won.
   She picks two tickets at random.
   Are her chances of winning at least one prize better or worse than Amy's? Explain your answer.

....

....

....

....

....

[3]

[Total 7 marks]

5 A bag contains counters that are either green or blue.
   • There are n green counters.
   • The number of blue counters is one more than the number of green counters.
Two counters are taken out of the bag at random without replacement.

Show that the probability that both counters are the same colour is $\dfrac{n}{2n+1}$.

[Total 5 marks]

Score:

24

Section Seven — Probability and Statistics

Venn Diagrams

1 The universal set ξ is the integers 1-20.

Set A is made up of the numbers generated by the sequence $2n + 1$ where n is a positive integer.

Set B is made up of the numbers generated by the sequence $\dfrac{n(n+1)}{2}$ where n is a positive integer.

a) Complete this Venn diagram to show the number of elements in each set.

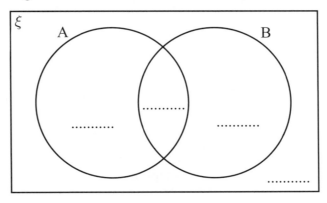

[3]

b) What is the probability that a randomly chosen element is in both set A and set B?

....

[1]

[Total 4 marks]

2 The Venn diagram on the right shows the number of students at a school who attended the school disco (D) and chess club (C).

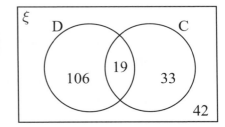

 a) What is the ratio of students attending the disco to the total number of students? Give your answer in its simplest form.

....

[2]

b) What is the probability that a randomly chosen student
   (i) attended chess club, given that they also went to the school disco?

....

[2]

   (ii) attended the disco, given that they only attended one event?

....

[2]

[Total 6 marks]

Section Seven — Probability and Statistics

3 Jack asked 80 people whether they like baking, running and shopping.
Half of the people only liked one activity. 10% of people liked all three activities.
22 people liked baking and running. 18 people liked shopping and running.
43 people liked baking and 35 liked shopping. Everyone liked at least one activity.

a) Complete this Venn diagram to show the number of elements in each set.

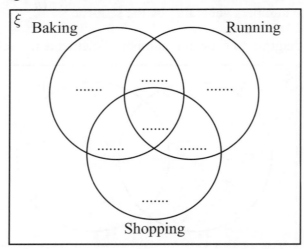

[5]

b) What is the probability that a randomly selected person liked baking, given that they liked at least two activities? Give your answer as a fraction in its simplest form.

....

[2]

[Total 7 marks]

4 In the Venn diagram on the right,
ξ = 50 people in a choir
P = people who play the piano
G = people who play the guitar.

Two different people in the choir are chosen at random.
Find the probability that they can both play the piano.

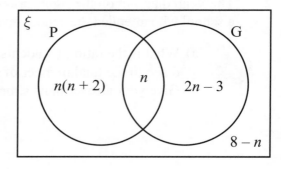

....

[Total 5 marks]

Score:

22

Section Seven — Probability and Statistics

Histograms

1 A cycling club decided to measure how long it took each of its members to complete a 1 mile course. 39 members took between 70 and 85 seconds to complete the course.

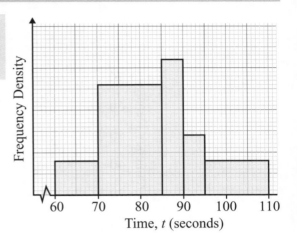

The histogram on the right shows the times recorded by the members.
How many members does the cycling club have?

....

[Total 4 marks]

2 A sample of 600 bouncy balls were individually weighed and the results are shown on the histogram below.

a) Estimate the mean weight of the bouncy balls.
   Give your answer to 1 d.p.

> Find the frequencies of each class by working out the proportion of the graph that each bar takes up.

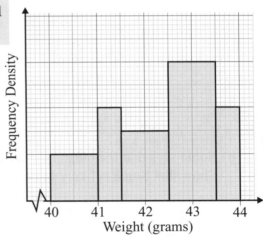

.... g
[5]

b) Sumi says, "The median weight of the bouncy balls is over 42.5 g."
   Is she correct? Explain your answer.

....

....

[2]

[Total 7 marks]

Section Seven — Probability and Statistics

3   The histogram shows the heights of the statues in a palace.

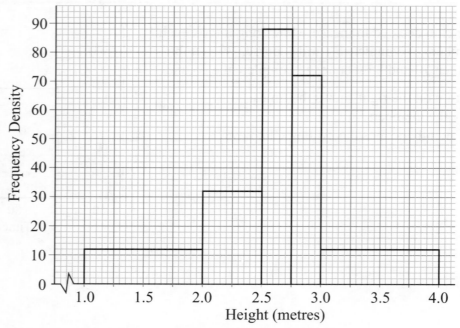

a) Work out an estimate for the percentage of statues that have a height between 1.75 metres and 2.75 metres.

.... %

[3]

b) Sonia says that the mean height of the statues is less than 2.5 metres. Show that Sonia is likely to be wrong.

[3]

c) What is the probability that a randomly chosen statue is over 3 metres tall, given that it's over 2 metres tall?

....

[2]

[Total 8 marks]

Score: ☐

19

Section Seven — Probability and Statistics

 ☐   ☐   ☐

Comparing Data Sets

1 This cumulative frequency graph shows how quickly tickets for a pantomime sold out in 2013. The table below summarises how quickly tickets for the same pantomime sold out in 2014.

Ticket Sales in 2014	
Time it took to sell out	24 minutes
Median	16 minutes
Interquartile range	3 minutes

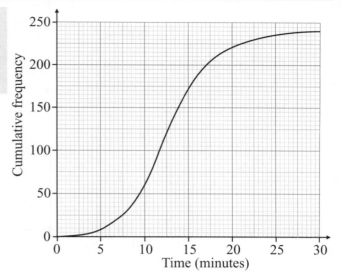

Compare the times it took tickets for the pantomime to sell in 2013 and 2014.

....

....

....

....

....

[Total 4 marks]

2 The box plot below shows the distribution of GCSE maths marks of pupils at Stonehill Academy. The table shows summary statistics of GCSE maths marks of pupils at Grimlock Secondary.

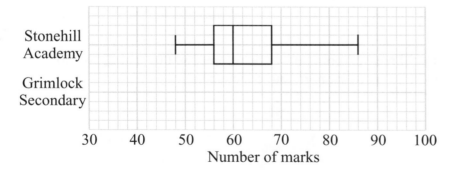

GCSE Maths Marks at Grimlock Secondary	
Lowest mark	36
Range	60
Median	72
Upper quartile	82
Interquartile range	14

a) Draw the box plot for Grimlock Secondary on the diagram above.

[2]

b) Compare the average and spread of the marks at Stonehill Academy and Grimlock Secondary.

....

....

....

[2]

[Total 4 marks]

3   The house prices of three-bedroom houses in two towns,
A and B, are shown in the histograms.

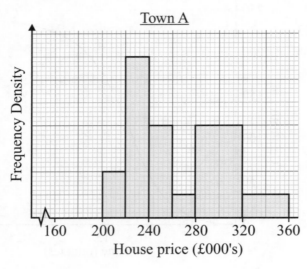

a) Decide whether each of these statements is correct. Give reasons for your answers.
   (i) "There is a greater range of three-bedroom house prices in town A."

....

....

....

[2]

   (ii) "There are more three-bedroom houses priced between £320 000 and £360 000 in town B
        than town A."

....

....

....

[2]

b) Is there a higher proportion of three-bedroom houses between £280 000 and £320 000
   in town A or town B? Show working to support your conclusion.

[4]

[Total 8 marks]

Score:

16

Section Seven — Probability and Statistics

Answers

Section One — Number

Pages 3-4: Fractions

1 a) Ratio of girls to boys in Year 7 is $3:2$, so fraction of Year 7 that are girls $= \frac{3}{3+2} = \frac{3}{5}$ *[1 mark]*.

   $20\% = \frac{1}{5}$ of girls in Year 7 have blonde hair, so $\frac{1}{5} \times \frac{3}{5} = \frac{3}{25}$ of the pupils in Year 7 are girls with blonde hair *[1 mark]*.

   Fraction of whole school that are Year 7 girls: $\frac{1}{5} \times \frac{3}{25} = \frac{3}{125}$ *[1 mark]*

   [3 marks available in total — as above]

   b) E.g. The answer to part a) would convert to a terminating decimal because the only prime factor of the denominator is 5.
   [1 mark for a correct conclusion based on part a)]

2 a) $\frac{a}{11} + \frac{b}{6} = \frac{6a+11b}{66}$ *[1 mark]*

   $\frac{25}{33} = \frac{50}{66}$, so $\frac{6a+11b}{66} = \frac{50}{66}$ and $6a + 11b = 50$ *[1 mark]*

   Putting in $a = 1$ gives $11b = 50 - 6 = 44$, so $b = 44 \div 11 = 4$
   [1 mark for both a and b]
   [3 marks available in total — as above]
   You might have to use trial and error to find the values of a and b.

   b) $\frac{25}{33}$ is equivalent to $\frac{75}{99}$ *[1 mark]* $= 0.\dot{7}\dot{5}$ *[1 mark]*
   [2 marks available in total — as above]
   You could also do this one by working out 25 ÷ 33.

3 Let $r = 0.14\dot{6}$. Then $100r = 14.\dot{6}$ and $1000r = 146.\dot{6}$
   $1000r - 100r = 146.\dot{6} - 14.\dot{6}$, so $900r = 132$
   $r = \frac{132}{900}$, so $1.14\dot{6} = 1\frac{132}{900}$

   $\frac{96}{180} = \frac{480}{900}$, so $\frac{96}{180} + 1.14\dot{6} = \frac{480}{900} + 1\frac{132}{900} = 1\frac{612}{900} = 1\frac{17}{25}$
   [5 marks available — 1 mark for a correct method for converting the recurring decimal to a fraction, 1 mark for a correct fraction, 1 mark for putting both fractions over a common denominator, 1 mark for adding the fractions, 1 mark for simplifying correctly]

4 $0.\dot{2} = \frac{2}{9}$, so $2.\dot{2} = 2\frac{2}{9} = \frac{20}{9}$

   Area of one tile $= \left(\frac{20}{9}\right)^2 = \frac{400}{81}$ cm²

   Heather will need $1600 \div \frac{400}{81} = 1600 \times \frac{81}{400} = 324$ tiles
   [4 marks available — 1 mark for writing the side length as a fraction, 1 mark for finding the area of the tile, 1 mark for dividing the total area by the area of one tile, 1 mark for the correct answer]

5 Let $r = 0.1\dot{2}\dot{7}$. Then $10r = 1.\dot{2}\dot{7}$ and $1000r = 127.\dot{2}\dot{7}$
   $1000r - 10r = 127.\dot{2}\dot{7} - 1.\dot{2}\dot{7}$, so $990r = 126$

   $r = \frac{126}{990} = \frac{14}{110} = \frac{7}{55} = \frac{35}{275}$

   $\frac{160}{1375} = \frac{32}{275}$

   So $\frac{38}{275}$ is the biggest.
   [4 marks available — 1 mark for a correct method for converting the recurring decimal to a fraction, 1 mark for a correct fraction, 1 mark for putting all converted fractions over a common denominator, 1 mark for stating which is biggest]

6 Let $r = 0.0\dot{4}$. Then $10r = 0.\dot{4}$ and $100r = 4.\dot{4}$
   $100r - 10r = 4.\dot{4} - 0.\dot{4}$, so $90r = 4$

   $r = \frac{4}{90} = \frac{2}{45}$, so $\frac{7x-3}{6} = \frac{2}{45}$

   $7x - 3 = \frac{12}{45} = \frac{4}{15}$

   $7x = 3 + \frac{4}{15} = \frac{49}{15}$, so $x = \frac{7}{15}$

[4 marks available — 1 mark for a correct method for converting the recurring decimal to a fraction, 1 mark for a correct fraction, 1 mark for a correct method for solving the equation, 1 mark for the correct answer]
There are other ways of rearranging the equation for this one.

Pages 5-6: Bounds

1 a) $4z^3 = \frac{(x^{\frac{1}{2}}y^{-3}z)^2}{y^{-5}} = \frac{xy^{-6}z^2}{y^{-5}} = xy^{-1}z^2$

   $4z = \frac{x}{y}$, so $z = \frac{x}{4y}$
   [3 marks available — 3 marks for the correct answer, otherwise 1 mark for simplifying the powers on the numerator, 1 mark for dividing both sides by z^2]

   b) Upper bound for $x = 6.85$, lower bound for $y = 1.15$
   Upper bound for $z = \frac{6.85}{4 \times 1.15} = 1.489... = 1.49$ (3 s.f.)
   [3 marks available — 1 mark for finding the upper bound of x, 1 mark for finding the lower bound of y, 1 mark for the correct answer]

2 Maximum possible score before the vault:
   upper bound $= 16.425 + 13.155 + 14.885 = 44.465$ *[1 mark]*
   Lowest possible leading score $= 60.145$
   Shannon's minimum score after the vault
   $= 60.145 + 0.05 = 60.195$ *[1 mark]*
   So lowest possible score for the vault
   $= 60.195 - 44.465 = 15.73$ *[1 mark]*
   [3 marks available in total — as above]

3 Lower bound for $c = 11.75$, upper bound for $a = 6.25$ *[1 mark]*
   So lower bound for scale factor $= 11.75 \div 6.25 = 1.88$ *[1 mark]*
   Lower bound for $b = 3.45$ *[1 mark]*
   Lower bound for $d = 3.45 \times 1.88 = 6.486$ cm *[1 mark]*
   [4 marks available in total — as above]

4 Lower bound for $S = 179.15$
   Upper bound for $S = 179.25$ *[1 mark for both]*
   Lower bound for $x = 59.5$
   Upper bound for $x = 60.5$ *[1 mark for both]*
   $S = \frac{x}{360} \times \pi r^2$, so $r^2 = \frac{360S}{x\pi}$ *[1 mark]*
   Lower bound for r: $r^2 = \frac{360 \times 179.15}{60.5 \times \pi} = 339.323...$,
   so $r = 18.420... = 18.42$ (2 d.p.) *[1 mark]*
   Upper bound for r: $r^2 = \frac{360 \times 179.25}{59.5 \times \pi} = 345.219...$,
   so $r = 18.580... = 18.58$ (2 d.p.) *[1 mark]*
   [5 marks available in total — as above]

5 Lower bound for $A = 2850$, upper bound for $A = 2950$
   Lower bound for $x = 96.95$, upper bound for $x = 97.05$
   Lower bound for $y = 78.85$, upper bound for $y = 78.95$
   [2 marks for all bounds correct, otherwise 1 mark for four or five bounds correct]
   Lower bound for θ: $\sin\theta = \frac{2 \times 2850}{97.05 \times 78.95} = 0.743...$
   so $\theta = \sin^{-1}(0.743...) = 48.066...°$ *[1 mark]*
   Upper bound for θ: $\sin\theta = \frac{2 \times 2950}{96.95 \times 78.85} = 0.771...$
   so $\theta = \sin^{-1}(0.771...) = 50.515...°$ *[1 mark]*
   Value of θ using the rounded values:
   $\sin\theta = \frac{2 \times 2900}{97.0 \times 78.9} = 0.757...$
   so $\theta = \sin^{-1}(0.757...) = 49.274...°$ *[1 mark]*
   Difference between lower bound and rounded value
   $= 49.274... - 48.066... = 1.207...°$
   Difference between upper bound and rounded value
   $= 50.515... - 49.274... = 1.241...°$ *[1 mark for both]*
   So maximum possible error $= 1.24°$ (3 s.f.) *[1 mark]*
   [7 marks available in total — as above]

Pages 7-8: Standard Form

1. $(3 \times 10^{11})^4 = 3^4 \times (10^{11})^4 = 81 \times 10^{44}$ *[1 mark]* $= 8.1 \times 10^{45}$ *[1 mark]*
[2 marks available in total — as above]

2. 50% of $6.4 \times 10^5 = 3.2 \times 10^5$ acres,
10% of $6.4 \times 10^5 = 0.64 \times 10^5$ acres,
5% of $6.4 \times 10^5 = 0.32 \times 10^5$ acres, *[1 mark for suitable method]*
so 65% $= 3.2 \times 10^5 + 0.64 \times 10^5 + 0.32 \times 10^5$
$= (3.2 + 0.64 + 0.35) \times 10^5 = 4.16 \times 10^5$ acres of woodland *[1 mark]*
If three-quarters are protected, then one quarter is not protected:
$4.16 \times 10^5 \div 4 = 1.04 \times 10^5 = 104\ 000$ acres are not protected *[1 mark]*.
[3 marks available in total — as above]

3. $\dfrac{25^2 \times 6}{2^2 \times 50^4} = \dfrac{25 \times 25 \times 6}{2 \times 2 \times 50 \times 50 \times 50 \times 50} = \dfrac{6}{2 \times 2 \times 2 \times 2 \times 50 \times 50}$
$= \dfrac{3}{2 \times 2 \times 2 \times 50 \times 50} = \dfrac{3}{2} \times \dfrac{1}{2 \times 2 \times 50 \times 50}$
$= \dfrac{3}{2} \times \dfrac{1}{10\ 000} = 1.5 \times 10^{-4}$
[3 marks available — 1 mark for expanding powers, 1 mark for cancelling common factors, 1 mark for the correct answer in standard form]
There are other ways to simplify this, but you'll get the same answer.

4. Upper bound for weight $= 4.25 \times 10^4 = 42\ 500$ N
Lower bound for area $= 25$ m^2
Upper bound for pressure $= 42\ 500 \div 25 = 1700$ N/m$^2 > 1600$ N/m^2, so it is not definitely safe for the shipping container to be transported on the cargo ship.
[3 marks available — 1 mark for finding the upper bound for weight and the lower bound for area, 1 mark for the upper bound for pressure, 1 mark for the conclusion]

5. Volume of salt in the Heron Sea = 12% of 1.4×10^{14}
$= 0.12 \times 1.4 \times 10^{14} = 1.68 \times 10^{13}$ litres *[1 mark]*
Volume of salt in the Cobalt Sea = 8% of 8.5×10^{12}
$= 0.08 \times 8.5 \times 10^{12} = 6.8 \times 10^{11}$ litres *[1 mark]*
Percentage decrease: $\dfrac{1.68 \times 10^{13} - 6.8 \times 10^{11}}{1.68 \times 10^{13}} \times 100$
$= 95.952...\% = 95.95\%$ (2 d.p.) *[1 mark]*
[3 marks available in total — as above]

6. 1.8×10^{12} kg $= 1.8 \times 10^{15}$ g
Number of muffins $= 1.8 \times 10^{15} \div 120 = 1.8 \times 10^{15} \div 1.2 \times 10^2$
$= \dfrac{1.8}{1.2} \times \dfrac{10^{15}}{10^2} = 1.5 \times 10^{13}$
Number of muffins eaten per person $= 1.5 \times 10^{13} \div 7.2$ billion
$= 1.5 \times 10^{13} \div 7.2 \times 10^9 = \dfrac{1.5}{7.2} \times \dfrac{10^{13}}{10^9} \approx 0.2 \times 10^4 = 2000$
The newspaper is not likely to be correct, as it would mean that last year every person in the world ate over 2000 muffins each (which is more than 5 per day).
[4 marks available — 1 mark for converting either mass, 1 mark for finding the number of muffins, 1 mark for estimating the number of muffins eaten per person, 1 mark for stating that the newspaper's claims are incorrect with a suitable explanation]

7. $a = 2^{10} \times 5^9$
$b = (3 \times 3) \times 10^6 = (3 \times 3) \times (2 \times 5)^6 = 2^6 \times 3^2 \times 5^6$ *[1 mark]*
$c = 24 \times 10^8 = 2 \times 2 \times 2 \times 3 \times (2 \times 5)^8 = 2^{11} \times 3 \times 5^8$ *[1 mark]*
LCM $= 2^{11} \times 3^2 \times 5^9$ *[1 mark]* $= 2^2 \times 3^2 \times (2 \times 5)^9 = 2^2 \times 3^2 \times 10^9$
$= 36 \times 10^9 = 3.6 \times 10^{10}$ *[1 mark]*
[4 marks available in total — as above]

Section Two — Algebra

Pages 9-10: Powers

1. $111^{\frac{1}{4}} \times 111^{\frac{1}{4}} = 111^{\frac{1}{4}+\frac{1}{4}} = 111^{\frac{1}{2}} = \sqrt{111}$
$10^2 = 100$ and $11^2 = 121$, so $\sqrt{111}$ lies between 10 and 11.
111 is just closer to 121 that 100, so $\sqrt{111} \approx 10.5$ to 3 s.f.
[2 marks available — 1 mark for using the rules of powers to simplify the expression, 1 mark for a sensible estimation to 3 s.f. (allow 10.4 or 10.6)]
You might have been tempted to estimate the quartic (4th) root of 111 and multiply the results together, but this would be very tricky.

2. $81^{\frac{3}{4}} = (81^{\frac{1}{4}})^3$ *[1 mark]* $= (\sqrt[4]{81})^3 = 3^3 = 27$ *[1 mark]*
[2 marks available in total — as above]

3. $a^7 \times (25a^6 b^{10} c^5)^{\frac{1}{2}} = \sqrt{25}\ a^{(6 \div 2)+7} b^{10 \div 2} c^{5 \div 2} = 5a^{10} b^5 c^{\frac{5}{2}}$
[2 marks available — 2 marks for the correct answer, otherwise 1 mark for at least 2 of 5, a^{10}, b^5 or $c^{\frac{5}{2}}$ correct]

4. $125^{\frac{1}{3}} = \sqrt[3]{125} = 5$ *[1 mark]* and $3^{-2} = \dfrac{1}{3^2} = \dfrac{1}{9}$ *[1 mark]*
So $125^{\frac{1}{3}} \times 3^{-2} = 5 \times \dfrac{1}{9} = \dfrac{5}{9} = 0.555... = 0.\dot{5}$ *[1 mark]*
[3 marks available in total — as above]

5. $\left(\dfrac{64}{27}\right)^{-\frac{1}{3}} = \left(\dfrac{27}{64}\right)^{\frac{1}{3}} = \sqrt[3]{\dfrac{27}{64}} = \dfrac{\sqrt[3]{27}}{\sqrt[3]{64}} = \dfrac{3}{4}$
[2 marks available — 1 mark for inverting the fraction and making the power positive, 1 mark for the correct answer]

6. $\left(\dfrac{729}{8x}\right)^{\frac{1}{3}} = \dfrac{9}{4}$, so $8x = 4^3 = 64$ *[1 mark]*, which means $x = 8$ *[1 mark]*
[2 marks available in total — as above]

7. $b = (4c + 3)^{\frac{1}{3}}$, so $b^3 = (4c + 3)^{\frac{1}{3} \times 3} = 4c + 3$ *[1 mark]*
and $b^6 = (4c + 3)^2 = 16c^2 + 24c + 9$ *[1 mark]*
So $a = 3b^3 + 2b^6 = 3(4c + 3) + 2(16c^2 + 24c + 9)$
$= 12c + 9 + 32c^2 + 48c + 18 = 32c^2 + 60c + 27$ *[1 mark]*
[3 marks available in total — as above]

8. $\left(\dfrac{64}{49}\right)^{-\frac{x}{y}} = \left(\dfrac{49}{64}\right)^{\frac{x}{y}} = \dfrac{343}{512}$, so $(\sqrt[y]{49})^x = 343$ and $(\sqrt[y]{64})^x = 512$
$\sqrt{49} = 7$ and $7^3 = 343$, and $\sqrt{64} = 8$ and $8^3 = 512$,
so $x = 3$ and $y = 2$
[3 marks available — 1 mark for inverting the fraction and making the power positive, 1 mark for forming two equations in terms of x and y, 1 mark for finding the values of x and y]
You have to use a bit of trial and error to find the values of x and y.

9. $2\frac{7}{9} = \dfrac{25}{9}$ and $3\frac{1}{3} = \dfrac{10}{3}$ *[1 mark for both]*
$\left(2\frac{7}{9}\right)^{-\frac{1}{2}} = \left(\dfrac{25}{9}\right)^{-\frac{1}{2}} = \left(\dfrac{9}{25}\right)^{\frac{1}{2}}$ *[1 mark]* $= \dfrac{3}{5}$ *[1 mark]*
$2^{-2} = \dfrac{1}{2^2} = \dfrac{1}{4}$ *[1 mark]*
So $\dfrac{\left(2\frac{7}{9}\right)^{-\frac{1}{2}} \times 3\frac{1}{3}}{2^{-2}} = \dfrac{\frac{3}{5} \times \frac{10}{3}}{\frac{1}{4}} = 2 \div \dfrac{1}{4} = 8$ *[1 mark]*
[5 marks available in total — as above]

Pages 11-12: Surds

1. $(\sqrt{2})^2 = 2$, $(\sqrt{2})^3 = 2\sqrt{2}$, $(\sqrt{2})^4 = 4$, $(\sqrt{2})^5 = 4\sqrt{2}$
So $\sqrt{2} + (\sqrt{2})^2 + (\sqrt{2})^3 + (\sqrt{2})^4 + (\sqrt{2})^5$
$= \sqrt{2} + 2 + 2\sqrt{2} + 4 + 4\sqrt{2} = 6 + 7\sqrt{2}$
[3 marks available — 3 marks for the correct answer, otherwise 2 marks for expanding all four brackets correctly, otherwise 1 mark for expanding two or three brackets correctly]

2. $\sqrt{343} = \sqrt{49 \times 7} = 7\sqrt{7}$ *[1 mark]*, $\dfrac{21}{\sqrt{7}} = \dfrac{21\sqrt{7}}{7} = 3\sqrt{7}$ *[1 mark]*
and $4\sqrt{252} = 4\sqrt{36 \times 7} = 24\sqrt{7}$ *[1 mark]*
So $\sqrt{343} + \dfrac{21}{\sqrt{7}} - 4\sqrt{252} = 7\sqrt{7} + 3\sqrt{7} - 24\sqrt{7}$
$= -14\sqrt{7}$ *[1 mark]*
[4 marks available in total — as above]

3. Using Pythagoras' theorem:
$a^2 = (6 + \sqrt{3})^2 - (3 + 2\sqrt{3})^2$ *[1 mark]*
$= (36 + 6\sqrt{3} + 6\sqrt{3} + 3) - (9 + 6\sqrt{3} + 6\sqrt{3} + 12)$
$= (39 + 12\sqrt{3}) - (21 + 12\sqrt{3})$ *[1 mark]*
$= 39 - 21 = 18$ *[1 mark]*
$a^2 = 18$, so $a = \sqrt{18} = 3\sqrt{2}$ cm *[1 mark]*
[4 marks available in total — as above]

4. $(\sqrt{5} - 6)^3 = (\sqrt{5} - 6)(\sqrt{5} - 6)(\sqrt{5} - 6)$
$= (5 - 6\sqrt{5} - 6\sqrt{5} + 36)(\sqrt{5} - 6)$
$= (41 - 12\sqrt{5})(\sqrt{5} - 6)$
$= 41\sqrt{5} - 246 - 60 + 72\sqrt{5} = 113\sqrt{5} - 306$
[3 marks available — 1 mark for expanding the first pair of brackets, 1 mark for expanding the new pair of brackets, 1 mark for the correct answer]

Answers

5 Volume $= \sqrt{5}\,(1 + \sqrt{5})(2 + 3\sqrt{5}) = (\sqrt{5} + 5)(2 + 3\sqrt{5})$
$\qquad = 2\sqrt{5} + 15 + 10 + 15\sqrt{5} = 25 + 17\sqrt{5}$ cm³
[4 marks available — 1 mark for multiplying either bracket by $\sqrt{5}$, 1 mark for multiplying the result by the remaining bracket, 1 mark for correct expansion, 1 mark for the correct answer]

6 $\dfrac{2\sqrt{3}}{3 + \sqrt{3}} = \dfrac{2\sqrt{3}(3 - \sqrt{3})}{(3 + \sqrt{3})(3 - \sqrt{3})} = \dfrac{6\sqrt{3} - 6}{9 - 3} = \dfrac{6\sqrt{3} - 6}{6} = \sqrt{3} - 1$

$\dfrac{2 + \sqrt{3}}{2 - \sqrt{3}} = \dfrac{(2 + \sqrt{3})(2 + \sqrt{3})}{(2 - \sqrt{3})(2 + \sqrt{3})} = \dfrac{7 + 4\sqrt{3}}{4 - 3} = \dfrac{7 + 4\sqrt{3}}{1} = 7 + 4\sqrt{3}$

So $\dfrac{2\sqrt{3}}{3 + \sqrt{3}} + \dfrac{2 + \sqrt{3}}{2 - \sqrt{3}} = (\sqrt{3} - 1) + (7 + 4\sqrt{3}) = 6 + 5\sqrt{3}$
[5 marks available — 2 marks for correctly rationalising the denominator of the first fraction (or 1 mark for multiplying by $(3 - \sqrt{3})$), 2 marks for correctly rationalising the denominator of the second fraction (or 1 mark for multiplying by $(2 + \sqrt{3})$), 1 mark for the correct answer]

7 $(1 + 2\sqrt{2})^2 = (1 + 2\sqrt{2})(1 + 2\sqrt{2}) = 1 + 2\sqrt{2} + 2\sqrt{2} + 8$
$\qquad = 9 + 4\sqrt{2}$ *[1 mark]*
So $\dfrac{(1 + 2\sqrt{2})^2}{\sqrt{2} - 1} = \dfrac{9 + 4\sqrt{2}}{\sqrt{2} - 1} = \dfrac{(9 + 4\sqrt{2})(\sqrt{2} + 1)}{(\sqrt{2} - 1)(\sqrt{2} + 1)}$ *[1 mark]*
$\qquad = \dfrac{17 + 13\sqrt{2}}{2 - 1}$ *[1 mark]* $= 17 + 13\sqrt{2}$ *[1 mark]*
[4 marks available in total — as above]

Pages 13-14: Quadratic Equations

1 Surface area of a sphere $= 4\pi r^2$
$36\pi x^2 + 48\pi x + 16\pi = 4\pi(9x^2 + 12x + 4) = 4\pi(3x + 2)^2$
So $(3x + 2)^2 = r^2$, which means the radius is $(3x + 2)$ cm
[3 marks available — 1 mark for taking out a factor of 4π, 1 mark for factorising, 1 mark for square rooting to find the answer]

2 a) $2x^2 - 3x - 35 = (2x + 7)(x - 5)$
[2 marks available — 1 mark for correct numbers in brackets, 1 mark for correct signs]

b) $2(2x - 1)^2 - 3(2x - 1) - 35 = 0$
$(2(2x - 1) + 7)((2x - 1) - 5) = 0$ *[1 mark]*
$(4x + 5)(2x - 6) = 0$ *[1 mark]*,
so $x = -1.25$ or $x = 3$ *[1 mark for both]*
[3 marks available in total — as above]

3 $\dfrac{x}{2x + 1} - \dfrac{x + 3}{x - 1} = 2$
$x(x - 1) - (x + 3)(2x + 1) = 2(x - 1)(2x + 1)$
$x^2 - x - 2x^2 - x - 6x - 3 = 2(2x^2 + x - 2x - 1)$
$-x^2 - 8x - 3 = 4x^2 - 2x - 2$
$0 = 5x^2 + 6x + 1 = (5x + 1)(x + 1)$, so $x = -0.2$ or $x = -1$
[4 marks available — 1 mark for multiplying through by $(x - 1)(2x + 1)$, 1 mark for expanding brackets and rearranging to give a quadratic in the standard format, 1 mark for factorising, 1 mark for both correct answers]

4 a) $3x^2 - 14x - 24 = (3x + 4)(x - 6)$
[2 marks available — 1 mark for correct numbers in brackets, 1 mark for correct signs]

b) $3x^2 - 14x - 24 = (3x + 4)^2$
$(3x + 4)(x - 6) = (3x + 4)^2$
$(3x + 4)(x - 6) - (3x + 4)^2 = 0$ *[1 mark]*
$(3x + 4)[(x - 6) - (3x + 4)] = 0$
$(3x + 4)(-2x - 10) = 0$ *[1 mark]*
So $x = -\dfrac{4}{3}$ *[1 mark]* or $x = -5$ *[1 mark]*
[4 marks available in total — as above]
Don't be tempted to cancel a factor of $(3x + 4)$ from each side of the equation — you'd only end up with one solution instead of two.

5 Surface area of a cylinder $= 2\pi rh + 2\pi r^2$
So $2\pi r + 2\pi r^2 = 31\pi$ (as $h = 1$) *[1 mark]*
$2r^2 + 2r - 31 = 0$ *[1 mark]*
$r = \dfrac{-2 \pm \sqrt{2^2 - (4 \times 2 \times -31)}}{2 \times 2} = \dfrac{-2 \pm \sqrt{252}}{4}$ *[1 mark]*
$\qquad = \dfrac{-2 \pm 6\sqrt{7}}{4} = \dfrac{-1 \pm 3\sqrt{7}}{2}$

The radius must be positive, so $r = \dfrac{-1 + 3\sqrt{7}}{2}$ m *[1 mark]*.
[4 marks available in total — as above]
You're asked for the exact value of r, so leave your answer in surd form.

6 $\dfrac{1}{x} + \dfrac{6}{x + 2} = 5$, so $x + 2 + 6x = 5x(x + 2)$
$7x + 2 = 5x^2 + 10x$
$0 = 5x^2 + 3x - 2 = (5x - 2)(x + 1)$, so $x = \dfrac{2}{5}$ or $x = -1$
$\dfrac{1}{1 - 3x}$ is positive when $x = -1$, so $\dfrac{1}{1 - 3(-1)} = \dfrac{1}{4}$.
[5 marks available — 1 mark for multiplying through by $x(x + 2)$, 1 mark for expanding brackets and rearranging to give a quadratic in the standard form, 1 mark for factorising, 1 mark for both correct values of x, 1 mark for the correct answer]

Pages 15-16: Completing the Square

1 $7 \div 2 = \dfrac{7}{2}$, so $a = \dfrac{7}{2}$ and the brackets are $\left(x + \dfrac{7}{2}\right)^2$ *[1 mark]*.
Expanding the brackets: $\left(x + \dfrac{7}{2}\right)^2 = x^2 + 7x + \dfrac{49}{4}$ *[1 mark]*
To complete the square: $11 - \dfrac{49}{4} = -\dfrac{5}{4}$, so $b = -\dfrac{5}{4}$ *[1 mark]*
So $x^2 + 7x + 11 = \left(x + \dfrac{7}{2}\right)^2 - \dfrac{5}{4}$.
[3 marks available in total — as above]

2 a) f(x) has a turning point at (2, 5), so the completed square form is $(x - 2)^2 + 5$. Expanding the brackets:
$f(x) = (x - 2)^2 + 5 = x^2 - 4x + 4 + 5 = x^2 - 4x + 9$
So $p = -4$ and $q = 9$.
[3 marks available — 1 mark for using the turning point to find the completed square form, 1 mark for expanding the brackets, 1 mark for the values of p and q]

b) $f(x - 2) - 3 = (x - 2 - 2)^2 + 5 - 3 = (x - 4)^2 + 2$, so the turning point on the transformed graph has coordinates (4, 2).
[2 marks available — 1 mark for each correct coordinate]
This is a translation by 2 units right and 3 units down, so you could add/subtract these values from the original turning point.

c)

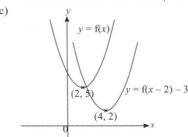

[2 marks available — 1 mark for x-translation, 1 mark for y-translation]

3 $r(x + 4)^2 + t = rx^2 + 8rx + 16r + t$
Equating coefficients with $3x^2 + sx + 29$ gives $3x^2 = rx^2$,
so $r = 3$ *[1 mark]*. $sx = 8rx$, so $s = 8r = 8 \times 3 = 24$ *[1 mark]*.
$29 = 16r + t$, so $t = 29 - (16 \times 3) = -19$ *[1 mark]*.
$y = 3(x + 4)^2 - 19$ has a turning point at $(-4, -19)$ *[1 mark]*.
[4 marks available in total — as above]

4 As the turning point is (4, 7), the equation of the curve can be written as $y = (x - 4)^2 + 7$ *[1 mark]*
Substituting in $x = 11$ gives
$y = (11 - 4)^2 + 7 = 49 + 7 = 56$ (as required) *[1 mark]*
[2 marks available in total — as above]

5 a) To find the turning point, complete the square:
$3x - x^2 + 5 = -(x^2 - 3x - 5)$
$-3 \div 2 = -\dfrac{3}{2}$, so the first bit is $-\left(x - \dfrac{3}{2}\right)^2$ *[1 mark]*.
Expanding brackets gives $-x^2 + 3x - \dfrac{9}{4}$
To complete the square: $5 - -\dfrac{9}{4} = \dfrac{29}{4}$ *[1 mark]*
So the completed square form is $-\left(x - \dfrac{3}{2}\right)^2 + \dfrac{29}{4}$
So the turning point has coordinates $\left(\dfrac{3}{2}, \dfrac{29}{4}\right)$ *[1 mark]*.
[3 marks available in total — as above]

b) The turning point will be a maximum as the coefficient of x^2 is negative (so the quadratic is n-shaped) *[1 mark]*.

6 a) Dividing the first two terms by 5: $5(x^2 + 4x) + 12$
$4 \div 2 = 2$, so the first bit is $5(x + 2)^2$
Expanding brackets gives: $5(x + 2)^2 = 5(x^2 + 4x + 4)$
$= 5x^2 + 20x + 20$
To complete the square: $12 - 20 = -8$
So $5x^2 + 20x + 12 = 5(x + 2)^2 - 8$
[4 marks available — 1 mark for dividing the first two terms by 5, 1 mark for finding the value of v, 1 mark for finding the value of w, 1 mark for the fully correct answer]

b) $5x^2 + 20x + 12 = 0$
So $5(x + 2)^2 - 8 = 0$
$(x + 2)^2 = \dfrac{8}{5}$
$x + 2 = \pm\sqrt{\dfrac{8}{5}}$, so $x = -2 \pm \sqrt{\dfrac{8}{5}}$
$x = -0.735$ (3 s.f.) or $x = -3.26$ (3 s.f.)
[2 marks available — 1 mark for rearranging the completed square, 1 mark for both correct x-values]

Pages 17-18: Algebraic Fractions

1 $\dfrac{2v^2 - 18}{v^2 + 3v} \times \dfrac{v^2 - v}{v^2 + 8v - 9} = \dfrac{2(v + 3)(v - 3)}{v(v + 3)} \times \dfrac{v(v - 1)}{(v + 9)(v - 1)}$
$= \dfrac{2(v - 3)}{v + 9}$
[5 marks available — 1 mark for factorising each of the numerators and denominators, 1 mark for the correct answer]

2 $\dfrac{1}{a} \div \dfrac{1}{b} = \dfrac{1}{a} \times b = \dfrac{1}{5x^2 - 80y^2} \times (40y - 10x)$
$= \dfrac{10(4y - x)}{5(x + 4y)(x - 4y)} = \dfrac{-10(x - 4y)}{5(x + 4y)(x - 4y)} = \dfrac{-2}{x + 4y}$
[4 marks available — 1 mark for multiplying by b, 1 mark for factorising a, 1 mark for factorising b, 1 mark for the correct answer]
Here you had to spot that (4y − x) = −1 × (x − 4y).

3 $\dfrac{3}{x} + \dfrac{2x}{x + 4} = \dfrac{3(x + 4) + x(2x)}{x(x + 4)} = \dfrac{2x^2 + 3x + 12}{x(x + 4)}$
[3 marks available — 1 mark for putting over a common denominator, 1 mark for adding numerators, 1 mark for correctly simplifying]

4 $\dfrac{x + 7}{x^2} \times \dfrac{x^2 + 2x}{x^2 - 49} \times \dfrac{6x - 42}{3x + 6}$
$= \dfrac{x + 7}{x^2} \times \dfrac{x(x + 2)}{(x + 7)(x - 7)} \times \dfrac{6(x - 7)}{3(x + 2)} = \dfrac{2}{x}$
[5 marks available — 1 mark for factorising each of the numerators and denominators of the second and third fractions, 1 mark for the correct answer]

5 $\dfrac{1}{x^2} + \dfrac{x + 3}{x - 2} - \dfrac{4}{x} = \dfrac{(x - 2) + x^2(x + 3) - 4x(x - 2)}{x^2(x - 2)}$
$= \dfrac{x - 2 + x^3 + 3x^2 - 4x^2 + 8x}{x^2(x - 2)} = \dfrac{x^3 - x^2 + 9x - 2}{x^2(x - 2)}$
[4 marks available — 1 mark for multiplying top and bottom of the first fraction by (x – 2), 1 mark for multiplying top and bottom of the second fraction by x², 1 mark for multiplying top and bottom of the third fraction by x(x – 2), 1 mark for simplifying]

6 $\dfrac{x^2 - 5}{2x^2 - 7x - 4} \times \dfrac{2x + 1}{x - \sqrt{5}} = \dfrac{(x + \sqrt{5})(x - \sqrt{5})}{(2x + 1)(x - 4)} \times \dfrac{2x + 1}{x - \sqrt{5}} = \dfrac{x + \sqrt{5}}{x - 4}$
[3 marks available — 1 mark for correctly factorising x² – 5, 1 mark for factorising the denominator of the first fraction, 1 mark for the correct answer]

7 $\dfrac{14x - 35}{2x^2 + x - 15} \div \dfrac{4xy - 12y}{2x^2y - 18y} = \dfrac{14x - 35}{2x^2 + x - 15} \times \dfrac{2x^2y - 18y}{4xy - 12y}$
$= \dfrac{7(2x - 5)}{(2x - 5)(x + 3)} \times \dfrac{2y(x + 3)(x - 3)}{4y(x - 3)}$
$= \dfrac{7}{2}$, so $\dfrac{14x - 35}{2x^2 + x - 15} \div \dfrac{4xy - 12y}{2x^2 - 18y} \equiv k$, where $k = \dfrac{7}{2}$
[6 marks available — 1 mark for inverting the second fraction and multiplying, 1 mark for factorising each of the numerators and denominators, 1 mark for the value of k]

Pages 19-20: Sequences

1 5th term $= \left(\dfrac{1}{2}\right)^5 = \dfrac{1}{2^5} = \dfrac{1}{32}$
8th term $= \left(\dfrac{1}{2}\right)^8 = \dfrac{1}{2^8} = \dfrac{1}{256}$ *[1 mark for both]*
Difference $= \dfrac{1}{32} - \dfrac{1}{256} = \dfrac{8}{256} - \dfrac{1}{256} = \dfrac{7}{256}$ *[1 mark]*
[2 marks available in total — as above]

2 a)
| Sequence: | 3 | | 9 | | 21 | | 39 |
First difference: 6   12   18
Second difference: 6   6 *[1 mark]*
Coefficient of $n^2 = 6 \div 2 = 3$
Actual sequence $- 3n^2$ sequence: 0 -3 -6 -9
Difference: -3 -3 -3
So this is a linear sequence with nth term $-3n + 3$ *[1 mark]*.
So the nth term of Justin's sequence is $3n^2 - 3n + 3$ *[1 mark]*.
[3 marks available in total — as above]

b) Set the sequences equal to each other and solve for n:
$93 - 6n = 3n^2 - 3n + 3$ *[1 mark]*
$0 = 3n^2 + 3n - 90$
$0 = n^2 + n - 30 = (n + 6)(n - 5)$ *[1 mark]*
So $n = -6$ or $n = 5$. n must be positive, so $n = 5$,
which gives a value of $93 - (6 \times 5) = 93 - 30 = 63$ *[1 mark]*.
[3 marks available in total — as above]
Check your answer by putting in into Justin's sequence.

3 nth term: $3n^2 - 4n + 1$
$(n + 1)$th term: $3(n + 1)^2 - 4(n + 1) + 1 = 3n^2 + 2n$ *[1 mark]*
Sum $= 3n^2 - 4n + 1 + 3n^2 + 2n = 6n^2 - 2n + 1$
So $6n^2 - 2n + 1 = 581$ *[1 mark]*
$6n^2 - 2n - 580 = 0$
$3n^2 - n - 290 = 0$, so $(3n + 29)(n - 10) = 0$ *[1 mark]*
So $n = -\dfrac{29}{3}$ or $n = 10$. n must be a positive integer, so $n = 10$.
So the two terms are the 10th and 11th terms, which are
$3(10)^2 - 4(10) + 1 = 261$ *[1 mark]*
and $3(11)^2 - 4(11) + 1 = 320$ *[1 mark]*
[5 marks available in total — as above]

4 Difference between the first and second terms:
$(8x - 29) - (6x + 1) = 2x - 30$
Difference between the second and third terms:
$(5x + 6) - (8x - 29) = -3x + 35$
In an arithmetic sequence, the difference between each pair of terms is the same, so $2x - 30 = -3x + 35$
$5x = 65$, which means $x = 13$.
So the first three terms are $6(13) + 1 = 79$, $8(13) - 29 = 75$ and $5(13) + 6 = 71$. The nth term of this sequence is $83 - 4n$, so the 20th term is $83 - 4(20) = 83 - 80 = 3$.
[6 marks available — 1 mark for finding the differences between both pairs of terms, 1 mark for setting these expressions equal to each other, 1 mark for solving to find the value of x, 1 mark for using the value of x to find the first three terms, 1 mark for finding an expression for the nth term, 1 mark for using this expression to find the 20th term]

5 Find the value of n for which $50 - \dfrac{1}{2}n^2 < 0$
$50 - \dfrac{1}{2}n^2 < 0$, so $100 - n^2 < 0$
$(10 + n)(10 - n) < 0$ *[1 mark]*
So $n < -10$ or $n > 10$. n must be a positive integer, so $n > 10$ *[1 mark]*, which means $n = 11$ is the first term that's less than 0.
The 11th term is $50 - \dfrac{1}{2}(11)^2 = 50 - 60.5 = -10.5$ *[1 mark]*.
[3 marks available in total — as above]
Quickly sketch the quadratic if you need to.

6 8th term of Kim's sequence $= (\sqrt{3})^8 = 3^4 = 81$ *[1 mark]*
Alex's sequence is quadratic, and the first two differences are 3 and 6, so the next differences will be 9, 12 and 15.
4th term $= 27 + 9 = 36$ *[1 mark]*, 5th term $= 36 + 12 = 48$,
6th term $= 48 + 15 = 63$ *[1 mark]*
Sum of terms $= 81 + 63 = 144 = 12^2$ *[1 mark]*
[4 marks available in total — as above]

Answers

Pages 21-22: Quadratic Inequalities

1   $x^2 + x - 56 = 0$ factorises to give $(x + 8)(x - 7) = 0$. The graph of
$y = x^2 + x - 56$ is a u-shaped quadratic that crosses the x-axis at
$x = -8$ and $x = 7$, and the graph is below 0 between these points.
So $-8 < x < 7$.
*[3 marks available — 1 mark for factorising the quadratic to
find the solutions, 1 mark for −8 and 7, 1 mark for correct
inequality symbols]*
Sketching a graph is always handy when solving quadratic inequalities.

2   $4x - x^2 = 0$ factorises to give $x(4 - x) = 0$, so $4x - x^2 \leq 0$ means
$x \leq 0$ and $x \geq 4$.

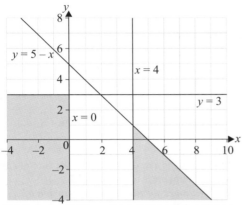

*[4 marks available — 1 mark for solving the quadratic inequality,
1 mark for drawing the lines x = 0, x = 4 and y = 3, 1 mark for
drawing the line y = 5 − x, 1 mark for shading the correct regions]*

3   Area of circle A = πr^2 cm^2
Area of circle B = $\pi(3r)^2$ cm^2 = $9\pi r^2$ cm^2
Sum of areas = $\pi r^2 + 9\pi r^2 = 10\pi r^2$ cm^2, so $10\pi r^2 > 160\pi$
$r^2 > 16$ so $r < -4$ or $r > 4$
r cannot be negative so $r > 4$. The smallest possible integer value
of r is 5, so the smallest possible radius of circle A is 5 cm and the
smallest possible radius of circle B is $3 \times 5 = 15$ cm.
*[3 marks available — 1 mark for finding an expression for the
sum of the areas, 1 mark for forming an inequality for the areas
and solving to find r, 1 mark for the correct radius of both circles]*

4   $3x^2 - x - 90 \geq 5x + 15$, so $3x^2 - 6x - 105 \geq 0$
Solve the quadratic equation $3x^2 - 6x - 105 = 0$
$x^2 - 2x - 35 = 0$
$(x + 5)(x - 7) = 0$
The graph of $y = 3x^2 - 6x - 105$ is a u-shaped quadratic that crosses
the x-axis at $x = -5$ and $x = 7$, and the graph is above 0 when $x \leq -5$
and $x \geq 7$.
*[4 marks available — 1 mark for rearranging the inequality,
1 mark for factorising the quadratic to find the solutions,
1 mark for −5 and 7, 1 mark for correct inequality symbols]*

5   a) The volume of cuboid A is $3x(x + 2) = 3x^2 + 6x$ cm^3. *[1 mark]*
The volume of cuboid B is $4x^2$ cm^3. *[1 mark]*
$3x^2 + 6x < 4x^2$ so $x^2 - 6x > 0$. *[1 mark]*
[3 marks available in total — as above]

   b) $x^2 - 6x = 0$ factorises to give $x(x - 6) = 0$ *[1 mark]*.
The graph of $y = x^2 - 6x$ is a u-shaped quadratic that crosses
the x-axis at $x = 0$ and $x = 6$, and the graph is positive (i.e. > 0)
when $x < 0$ and $x > 6$ *[1 mark]*.
The smallest positive integer solution is $x = 7$ *[1 mark]*,
so the smallest possible volume of cuboid B is
$4 \times 7 \times 7 = 196$ cm^3. *[1 mark]*
[4 marks available in total — as above]

6   $x^2 \leq \dfrac{23x - 45}{2}$, so $2x^2 \leq 23x - 45$, which means $2x^2 - 23x + 45 \leq 0$.
$2x^2 - 23x + 45 = 0$ factorises to give $(2x - 5)(x - 9) = 0$. The graph
of $y = 2x^2 - 23x + 45$ is a u-shaped quadratic that crosses the x-axis
at $x = 2.5$ and $x = 9$, and the graph is below 0 between these points.
So $2.5 \leq x \leq 9$.
*[4 marks available — 1 mark for rearranging the inequality,
1 mark for factorising the quadratic to find the solutions,
1 mark for 2.5 and 9, 1 mark for correct inequality symbols]*

Pages 23-24: Iterative Methods

1   a) Put $x = 1$ into the equation of each graph:
$(1 - 1)^2(2(1) + 5) = 0$ and $10(1)^2 - 8(1) - 2 = 0$
The y-value is the same on each graph, so the graphs must
intersect at that point.
*[2 marks available — 1 mark for calculating the y-value for
both graphs, 1 mark for stating that the values are equal so
the graphs must intersect]*

   b) At the points of intersection, the graphs cross so they must be
equal. So $(x - 1)^2(2x + 5) = 10x^2 - 8x - 2$
$(x^2 - 2x + 1)(2x + 5) = 10x^2 - 8x - 2$
$2x^3 + 5x^2 - 4x^2 - 10x + 2x + 5 = 10x^2 - 8x - 2$
$2x^3 - 9x^2 + 7 = 0$
*[3 marks available — 1 mark for expanding two of the
brackets on the LHS, 1 mark for multiplying the product by
the third bracket, 1 mark for simplifying]*

   c) Put $x = 4$ and $x = 5$ into the expression from b):
$x = 4$: $2(4)^3 - 9(4)^2 + 7 = 128 - 144 + 7 = -9$
$x = 5$: $2(5)^3 - 9(5)^2 + 7 = 250 - 225 + 7 = 32$
There is a sign change between $x = 4$ and $x = 5$,
so there must be a solution in the interval.
*[2 marks available — 1 mark for finding the values when
x = 4 and x = 5, 1 mark for stating that a sign change means
there's a root]*

   d)

x	$2x^3 - 9x^2 + 7$	
4	−9	Negative
5	32	Positive
4.1	−6.448	Negative
4.2	−3.584	Negative
4.3	−0.396	Negative
4.4	3.128	Positive
4.31	−0.058918	Negative
4.32	0.281536	Positive

So $x = 4.3$ to 1 d.p.
*[4 marks available — 3 marks for a correctly filled in table,
1 mark for the correct value of x, otherwise 2 marks for 5 or 6
rows correct or 1 mark for 3 or 4 rows correct]*

2   a) Put $x = 1$ and $x = 1.5$ into the expression:
$x = 1$: $(1)^3 + 3(1)^2 - 5 = 1 + 3 - 5 = -1$
$x = 1.5$: $(1.5)^3 + 3(1.5)^2 - 5 = 3.375 + 6.75 - 5 = 5.125$
There is a sign change between $x = 1$ and $x = 1.5$,
so there must be a solution in the interval.
*[2 marks available — 1 mark for finding the values when
x = 1 and x = 1.5, 1 mark for stating that a sign change
means there's a root]*

   b) $x_0 = 1$ \qquad $x_1 = 1.111111...$ \qquad $x_2 = 1.103835...$
$x_3 = 1.103803...$ \qquad $x_4 = 1.103803...$
$x_3 = x_4$ to 5 d.p. so $x = 1.10380$ to 5 d.p.
*[3 marks available — 2 marks for carrying out the iteration an
appropriate number of times, 1 mark for the correct value of x]*

3   a) $x^3 - 3x^2 - 4x + 10 = 0$
$x^3 - 3x^2 = 4x - 10$
$x^2(x - 3) = 4x - 10$ *[1 mark]*
$x^2 = \dfrac{4x - 10}{x - 3}$ *[1 mark]*
$x = \pm\sqrt{\dfrac{4x - 10}{x - 3}}$, so $a = 4$ and $b = 3$ *[1 mark]*
[3 marks available in total — as above]

   b) $x_0 = 1.5$ \qquad $x_1 = 1.6329...$ \qquad $x_2 = 1.5927...$
$x_3 = 1.6058...$ \qquad $x_4 = 1.6016...$ \qquad $x_5 = 1.6030...$
$x_4 = x_5$ to 3 s.f. so $x = 1.60$ to 3 s.f.
*[3 marks available — 2 marks for carrying out the iteration an
appropriate number of times, 1 mark for the correct value of x]*

Pages 25-26: Simultaneous Equations

1   $2x - y = x + 4$, so $x = y + 4$
Then $(y + 4)^2 + 4y^2 = 37$ *[1 mark]*
$y^2 + 8y + 16 + 4y^2 = 37$
$5y^2 + 8y - 21 = 0$ *[1 mark]*
$(5y - 7)(y + 3) = 0$ *[1 mark]*, so $y = 1.4$ or $y = -3$ *[1 mark]*
When $y = 1.4$, $x = 1.4 + 4 = 5.4$
When $y = -3$, $x = -3 + 4 = 1$
So the solutions are $x = 5.4$, $y = 1.4$ and $x = 1$, $y = -3$ *[1 mark]*
[5 marks available in total — as above]

2   Area $= (2x \times x) + (y \times 3y) = 2x^2 + 3y^2$
So $2x^2 + 3y^2 = 83$
Base length $= 2x + y$, so $2x + y = 9$, which means $y = 9 - 2x$
So $2x^2 + 3(9 - 2x)^2 = 83$
$2x^2 + 243 - 108x + 12x^2 = 83$
$14x^2 - 108x + 160 = 0$
$7x^2 - 54x + 80 = 0$, so $(7x - 40)(x - 2) = 0$
So $x = 40 \div 7 = 5.714...$ or $x = 2$. x is an integer so $x = 2$.
When $x = 2$, $y = 9 - 2(2) = 9 - 4 = 5$.
[5 marks available — 1 mark for forming equations for the area and base length, 1 mark for substituting an expression for x or y into the quadratic equation, 1 mark for factorising the quadratic equation, 1 mark for the correct value of x, 1 mark for the correct value of y]

3   $7x - y = 25$, so $y = 7x - 25$
Then $x^2 + (7x - 25)^2 = 25$ *[1 mark]*
$x^2 + 49x^2 - 350x + 625 = 25$
$50x^2 - 350x + 600 = 0$
$x^2 - 7x + 12 = 0$
$(x - 3)(x - 4) = 0$ *[1 mark]*, so $x = 3$ or $x = 4$ *[1 mark]*
When $x = 3$, $y = (7 \times 3) - 25 = 21 - 25 = -4$
When $x = 4$, $y = (7 \times 4) - 25 = 28 - 25 = 3$
So the line intersects the circle at $(3, -4)$ and $(4, 3)$ *[1 mark]*
Change in $x = 4 - 3 = 1$, change in $y = 3 - (-4) = 7$ *[1 mark for both]*
Length $AB = \sqrt{1^2 + 7^2} = \sqrt{50} = 5\sqrt{2}$ *[1 mark]*
[6 marks available in total — as above]

4   Face A: $P = \dfrac{F}{A}$, so $10 = \dfrac{120}{A}$, which means area of face $A = 12$ m^2
So $(x + 1) \times y = 12$ or $xy + y = 12$ (1)
Face B: $P = \dfrac{F}{A}$, so $7.5 = \dfrac{120}{A}$, which means area of face $B = 16$ m^2
So $(x + 3) \times y = 16$ or $xy + 3y = 16$ (2)
(2) − (1): $2y = 4$, so $y = 2$
$xy + y = 12$, so $2x + 2 = 12$, which means $2x = 10$ so $x = 5$
Volume $= (5 + 1) \times (5 + 3) \times 2 = 6 \times 8 \times 2 = 96$ m^3
[6 marks available — 1 mark for finding the areas of faces A and B, 1 mark for finding an equation for the area of face A, 1 mark for finding an equation for the area of face B, 1 mark for solving the simultaneous equations to find the value of y, 1 mark for finding the value of x, 1 mark for the correct volume]
There are other ways of doing one — you could start by finding expressions for the pressure exerted by each face in terms of x and y.

5   $2x - 5 = -x^2 + 15x - 41$ *[1 mark]*
$x^2 - 13x + 36 = 0$
$(x - 4)(x - 9) = 0$ *[1 mark]*, so $x = 4$ or $x = 9$ *[1 mark]*
When $x = 4$, $y = 2(4) - 5 = 3$
When $x = 9$, $y = 2(9) - 5 = 13$ *[1 mark for both y-values]*
$ABDC$ is a trapezium with $CD = 9 - 4 = 5$, $AC = 3$ and $BD = 13$
[1 mark for all lengths correct],
so area $= \dfrac{1}{2}(3 + 13) \times 5 = 40$ units^2 *[1 mark]*
[6 marks available in total — as above]

Pages 27-28: Proof

1   LHS: $(2n + 1)^3 - 1 \equiv (4n^2 + 4n + 1)(2n + 1) - 1$
$\equiv 8n^3 + 4n^2 + 8n^2 + 4n + 2n + 1 - 1$
$\equiv 8n^3 + 12n^2 + 6n \equiv 2n(4n^2 + 6n + 3) \equiv$ RHS
[3 marks available — 1 mark for correctly expanding cubed bracket, 1 mark for simplifying, 1 mark for factorising to show that LHS ≡ RHS]

2   Take three rational numbers, $\dfrac{a}{b}$, $\dfrac{c}{d}$ and $\dfrac{e}{f}$ (where a, b, c, d, e and f are all integers and b, d and $f \neq 0$).
Their product is $\dfrac{a}{b} \times \dfrac{c}{d} \times \dfrac{e}{f} = \dfrac{ace}{bdf}$ *[1 mark]*.
The product of integers is also an integer, so ace and bdf are both integers, which means that $\dfrac{ace}{bdf}$ is rational *[1 mark]*.
[2 marks available in total — as above]

3   If a and b are both odd, then let $a = 2m + 1$ and $b = 2n + 1$ for integers m and n. Then $a + b = (2m + 1) + (2n + 1) = 2m + 2n + 2 = 2(m + n + 1) = 2x$ (where $x = m + n + 1$) *[1 mark]*. So $a + b$ is always even, which means that $(a + b)^{40} = (2x)^{40} = 2^{40}x^{40} = 2(2^{39}x^{40}) = 2y$, where $y = (2^{39}x^{40})$ *[1 mark]*, which is even.
[2 marks available in total — as above]

4   Take three consecutive numbers, n, $n + 1$ and $n + 2$.
Their cubes are n^3, $(n + 1)^3 = (n^2 + 2n + 1)(n + 1)$
$= n^3 + n^2 + 2n^2 + 2n + n + 1 = n^3 + 3n^2 + 3n + 1$
and $(n + 2)^3 = (n^2 + 4n + 4)(n + 2) = n^3 + 2n^2 + 4n^2 + 8n + 4n + 8$
$= n^3 + 6n^2 + 12n + 8$.
Their sum is $n^3 + n^3 + 3n^2 + 3n + 1 + n^3 + 6n^2 + 12n + 8$
$= 3n^3 + 9n^2 + 15n + 9 = 3(n^3 + 3n^2 + 5n + 3) = 3x$
(where $x = n^3 + 3n^2 + 5n + 3$).
Any integer multiplied by 3 is a multiple of 3, so the sum of any three consecutive cube numbers is a multiple of 3.
[4 marks available — 1 mark for the correct expansion of $(n + 1)^3$, 1 mark for the correct expansion of $(n + 2)^3$, 1 mark for adding the terms and simplifying the result, 1 mark for writing as a multiple of 3]

5   Max's number $= 5n + 1$ for some integer n
The square of Max's number is $(5n + 1)^2 = (5n + 1)(5n + 1)$
$= 25n^2 + 10n + 1$
Samira's number $= 5n - 3$ and the square of her number is
$(5n - 3)(5n - 3) = 25n^2 - 30n + 9$
Difference $= (25n^2 + 10n + 1) - (25n^2 - 30n + 9) = 40n - 8$
$= 8(5n - 1) = 8x$ (where $x = 5n - 1$)
Any integer multiplied by 8 is a multiple of 8, so the difference between the squares of their numbers is a multiple of 8.
[5 marks available — 1 mark for finding an expression for Max's number, 1 mark for finding an expression for Samira's number, 1 mark for squaring both numbers, 1 mark for finding the difference between the squares, 1 mark for writing as a multiple of 8]
Here, you could have written the difference as $(5n + 1)^2 - (5n - 3)^2$ and used the difference of two squares to find the expression $40n - 8$.

6   $3^8 - 7^4 = (3^4)^2 - (7^2)^2 = (3^4 + 7^2)(3^4 - 7^2)$
        $= (81 + 49)(81 - 49) = 130 \times 32$
        $= 13 \times 10 \times 32 = 13x$ (where $x = 10 \times 32$)
Any integer multiplied by 13 is a multiple of 13, so $3^8 - 7^4$ is a multiple of 13.
[3 marks available — 1 mark for factorising using the difference of two squares, 1 mark for finding the value of each factor, 1 mark for writing as a multiple of 13]

7   $15^{12} + 12^{16} = (3 \times 5)^{12} + (3 \times 2^2)^{16}$
           $= (3^{12} \times 5^{12}) + (3^{16} \times 2^{32})$ *[1 mark]*
           $= 3^2[(3^{10} \times 5^{12}) + (3^{14} \times 2^{32})]$ *[1 mark]*
           $= 9[(3^{10} \times 5^{12}) + (3^{14} \times 2^{32})]$
           $= 9x$ (where $x = (3^{10} \times 5^{12}) + (3^{14} \times 2^{32})$) *[1 mark]*
Any integer multiplied by 9 is a multiple of 9, so $15^{12} + 12^{16}$ is a multiple of 9.
[3 marks available — as above]

Pages 29-30: Functions

1   a) $fg(4) = f(g(4)) = f(4^2 + 4) = f(20) = \sqrt{2(20) - 8} = \sqrt{32} = 4\sqrt{2}$
[2 marks available — 1 mark for finding the value of g(4), 1 mark for using this value to find fg(4), giving the answer as a simplified surd]
You could have found an expression for fg(x) and put in x = 4.

    b) $gf(x) = g(f(x)) = g(\sqrt{2x - 8}) = (\sqrt{2x - 8})^2 + 4$ *[1 mark]*
             $= 2x - 8 + 4 = 2x - 4$ *[1 mark]*
[2 marks available in total — as above]

Answers

c) Write out $x = f(y)$: $x = \sqrt{2y - 8}$ *[1 mark]*
Rearrange to make y the subject: $x^2 = 2y - 8$ *[1 mark]*
$x^2 + 8 = 2y$
$y = \dfrac{x^2 + 8}{2}$, so $f^{-1}(x) = \dfrac{x^2 + 8}{2}$ *[1 mark]*
[3 marks available in total — as above]

2 Write out $x = f(y)$: $x = \dfrac{y + 5}{2}$ *[1 mark]*
Rearrange to make y the subject: $2x = y + 5$
$y = 2x - 5$, so $f^{-1}(x) = 2x - 5$ *[1 mark]*
Write out $x = g(y)$: $x = 3y - 10$ *[1 mark]*
Rearrange to make y the subject: $x + 10 = 3y$
$y = \dfrac{x + 10}{3}$, so $g^{-1}(x) = \dfrac{x + 10}{3}$ *[1 mark]*
When $f^{-1}(x) = g^{-1}(x)$, $2x - 5 = \dfrac{x + 10}{3}$ *[1 mark]*
$6x - 15 = x + 10$
$5x = 25$ so $x = 5$ *[1 mark]*
[6 marks available in total — as above]

3 $fg(x) = f(g(x)) = f(\sin x) = 2\sin x - 1$ *[1 mark]*
$2\sin x - 1 = 0$
$2\sin x = 1$
$\sin x = \dfrac{1}{2}$ *[1 mark]*
So $x = 30°$ *[1 mark]* and $x = 180° - 30° = 150°$ *[1 mark]*
[4 marks available in total — as above]
$\sin 30° = ½$ is one of the common trig values you should know.
You need to use the symmetry of the graph to find the second value.

4 a) $fgg(x) = f(g(g(x))) = f(g(x + 2))$
$= f((x + 2) + 2) = f(x + 4)$ *[1 mark]*
$= (x + 4)^2 + 4(x + 4) + 3$ *[1 mark]*
$= x^2 + 8x + 16 + 4x + 16 + 3$
$= x^2 + 12x + 35$ *[1 mark]*
[3 marks available in total — as above]

b) $fgg(x) = 0$ means that $x^2 + 12x + 35 = 0$
$(x + 7)(x + 5) = 0$, so $x = -7$ or $x = -5$
[2 marks available — 1 mark for setting expression from part a) equal to 0 and factorising, 1 mark for both correct x-values]

5 $h^{-1}(x) = \sqrt[3]{x}$ *[1 mark]*
$fgh^{-1}(x) = f(g(h^{-1}(x))) = f(g(\sqrt[3]{x}\,))$
$= f((\sqrt[3]{x})^2 + 3(\sqrt[3]{x}\,))$ *[1 mark]* $= f(x^{\frac{2}{3}} + 3x^{\frac{1}{3}})$ *[1 mark]*
$= 3(x^{\frac{2}{3}} + 3x^{\frac{1}{3}}) + 1$
$= 3x^{\frac{2}{3}} + 9x^{\frac{1}{3}} + 1$ *[1 mark]*
[4 marks available in total — as above]

6 $fg(x) = f(g(x)) = f(2x + 1) = \dfrac{4(2x + 1)}{(2x + 1) + 9} = \dfrac{8x + 4}{2x + 10}$
$= \dfrac{4x + 2}{x + 5}$ *[1 mark]*
So $\dfrac{4x + 2}{x + 5} = x$ *[1 mark]*
$4x + 2 = x(x + 5)$
$4x + 2 = x^2 + 5x$ *[1 mark]*
$0 = x^2 + x - 2 = (x + 2)(x - 1)$ *[1 mark]*
So $x = -2$ or $x = 1$ *[1 mark for both]*
[5 marks available in total — as above]

Section Three — Graphs

Pages 31-32: Coordinates and Ratio

1 a) Difference in x-coordinates from A to M: $4 - -2 = 6$
M is the midpoint of AB, so difference in x-coordinates from M to $B = 6$, so x-coordinate of $B = 4 + 6 = 10$ *[1 mark]*,
Difference in y-coordinates from A to M: $5 - 2 = 3$,
so difference in y-coordinates from M to $B = 3$,
so y-coordinate of $B = 5 + 3 = 8$ *[1 mark]*.
So the coordinates of B are $(10, 8)$.
[2 marks available in total — as above]

b) Difference in x-coordinates from M to B: $10 - 4 = 6$
Difference in y-coordinates from M to B: $8 - 5 = 3$
P is $\dfrac{1}{3}$ of the way along MB,
so the x-coordinate of P is $4 + (\dfrac{1}{3} \times 6) = 6$
and the y-coordinate of P is $5 + (\dfrac{1}{3} \times 3) = 6$
So the coordinates of P are $(6, 6)$.
Difference between x-coordinates of A and P: $6 - -2 = 8$
Difference between x-coordinates of A and B: $10 - -2 = 12$
so the ratio $AP : AB = 8 : 12 = 2 : 3$
[3 marks available — 1 mark for a correct method to find the coordinates of P, 1 mark for the correct coordinates of P, 1 mark for the correct ratio]
Instead of finding the coordinates of P, you could have found AP and AB in terms of MP and used this to find the ratio.

2 Coordinates of C are $(2 + 4, -1) = (6, -1)$
Coordinates of M are $(2 + 2, -1 + 2) = (4, 1)$
Difference in x-coordinates from E to M: $4 - 0 = 4$
Difference in x-coordinates from M to C: $6 - 4 = 2$
So $EM : MC = 4 : 2 = 2 : 1$
[3 marks available — 1 mark for finding the coordinates of C and M, 1 mark for finding the differences between the x- or y-coordinates of E & M and M & C, 1 mark for the correct ratio]

3 Difference in x-coordinates from E to B: $6 - 0 = 6$
Difference in y-coordinates from E to B: $4 - -4 = 8$
P is $\dfrac{3}{4}$ of the way along EB, so has x-coordinate $0 + \dfrac{3}{4} \times 6 = 4.5$
and y-coordinate $-4 + \dfrac{3}{4} \times 8 = 2$, so P has coordinates $(4.5, 2)$.
$PF^2 = (6 - 4.5)^2 + (0 - 2)^2 = 6.25$, so $PF = \sqrt{6.25} = 2.5$.
[4 marks available — 1 mark for correct difference in x- and y-coordinates of E and B, 1 mark for correct coordinates of P, 1 mark for using Pythagoras to find PF², 1 mark for the correct answer]

4 Difference in x-coordinates from A to M: $3 - -2 = 5$
M is the midpoint of AC, so difference in x-coordinates from M to $C = 5$, so x-coordinate of $C = 3 + 5 = 8$
C has the same y-coordinate as D, so the coordinates of C are $(8, 2)$
Difference in x-coordinates from M to C: $8 - 3 = 5$
Difference in y-coordinates from M to C: $2 - 4.5 = -2.5$
N is $\dfrac{3}{5}$ of the way along MC,
so the x-coordinate of N is $3 + \dfrac{3}{5} \times 5 = 6$
and the y-coordinate of N is $4.5 + \dfrac{3}{5} \times -2.5 = 3$
So the coordinates of N are $(6, 3)$.
B has the same y-coordinate as A, and the difference in x-coordinates of C and D is $8 - -5 = 13$, so the x-coordinate of B is $-2 + 13 = 11$. So B has coordinates $(11, 7)$.
Distance $NB^2 = (11 - 6)^2 + (7 - 3)^2 = 5^2 + 4^2 = 41$
$NB = \sqrt{41}$
[6 marks available — 1 mark for the correct coordinates of C, 1 mark for a correct method to find the coordinates of N, 1 mark for correct coordinates of N, 1 mark for the correct coordinates of B, 1 mark for a correct method to find the distance NB, 1 mark for the correct answer]
There are different ways to find the coordinates of N and C.

Pages 33-34: Perpendicular Lines

1 Gradient of L_1: $\dfrac{20 - 6}{11 - 4} = \dfrac{14}{7} = 2$,
so gradient of line $L_2 = -1 \div 2 = -\dfrac{1}{2}$
L_2 passes through $(28, 0)$, so $0 = -\dfrac{1}{2}(28) + c$
$0 = -14 + c$, so $c = 14$
So the equation of line L_2 is $y = -\dfrac{1}{2}x + 14$
[3 marks available — 1 mark for finding the gradient of line L_1, 1 mark for finding the gradient of L_2, 1 mark for the correct answer]

2 Gradient of $SQ = 4$

The diagonals of a kite cross at right angles so are perpendicular, so gradient of $PR = -\frac{1}{4}$.

Point R has coordinates $(8, 15)$, so $15 = -\frac{1}{4}(8) + c$

$15 = -2 + c$, so $c = 17$

So the equation of PR is $y = -\frac{1}{4}x + 17$

[3 marks available — 1 mark for stating that the diagonals of a kite are perpendicular, 1 mark for finding the gradient of PR, 1 mark for the correct answer]

3 Equation of L_1 is $x + 5y = 100$, or $y = -\frac{1}{5}x + 20$, so has gradient $-\frac{1}{5}$.

L_2 is perpendicular to L_1 so has gradient $-1 \div -\frac{1}{5} = 5$.

L_2 passes through $(2, 4)$, so $4 = 5(2) + c$

$4 = 10 + c$, so $c = -6$

So the equation of line L_2 is $y = 5x - 6$

At M, $-\frac{1}{5}x + 20 = 5x - 6$

$26 = \frac{26}{5}x$, so $x = 5$

When $x = 5$, $y = 5(5) - 6 = 25 - 6 = 19$

So the coordinates of M are $(5, 19)$.

[5 marks available — 1 mark for finding the gradient of L_1, 1 mark for finding the gradient of L_2, 1 mark for finding the equation of L_2, 1 mark for setting the equations for L_1 and L_2 equal to each other and solving to find x or y, 1 mark for the correct answer]

Check your answer by putting your x-coordinate into the equation of L_1 and checking you get the correct y-coordinate.

4 Equation of L_1 is $2y - x = 14$, or $y = \frac{1}{2}x + 7$ so has gradient $\frac{1}{2}$

L_2 is perpendicular to L_1 so has gradient $-1 \div \frac{1}{2} = -2$.

L_2 passes through point $(6, 10)$ so $10 = -2(6) + c$

$10 = -12 + c$, so $c = 22$. So the equation of L_2 is $y = -2x + 22$

R is the y-intercept of L_2, so the y-coordinate of R is 22.

RQ is horizontal so the y-coordinate of Q is 22

Q lies on L_1 so $22 = \frac{1}{2}x + 7$

$15 = \frac{1}{2}x$ so $x = 30$

So the coordinates of Q are $(30, 22)$.

[5 marks available — 1 mark for finding the gradient of L_1, 1 mark for finding the gradient of L_2, 1 mark for finding the equation of L_2, 1 mark for finding the y-coordinate of Q, 1 mark for the correct answer]

5 Equation of L_1 is $2x + 3y = 12$, or $y = -\frac{2}{3}x + 4$, so has gradient $-\frac{2}{3}$.

L_2 is parallel to L_1, so also has gradient $-\frac{2}{3}$.

L_2 passes through $(6, 13)$, so $13 = -\frac{2}{3}(6) + c_2$

$13 = -4 + c_2$, so $c_2 = 17$. So the equation of L_2 is $y = -\frac{2}{3}x + 17$.

L_3 is perpendicular to L_1 and L_2 so has gradient $\frac{3}{2}$.

It passes through $(3, 2)$ so $2 = \frac{3}{2}(3) + c_3$

$2 = \frac{9}{2} + c_3$, so $c_3 = -\frac{5}{2}$. So the equation of L_3 is $y = \frac{3}{2}x - \frac{5}{2}$

When L_2 and L_3 intersect, $-\frac{2}{3}x + 17 = \frac{3}{2}x - \frac{5}{2}$

$\frac{39}{2} = \frac{13}{6}x$ so $x = 9$.

When $x = 9$, $y = -\frac{2}{3}(9) + 17 = -6 + 17 = 11$

So L_2 and L_3 intersect at $(9, 11)$.

[6 marks available — 1 mark for finding the gradient of L_1, 1 mark for finding the equation of L_2, 1 mark for finding the gradient of L_3, 1 mark for finding the equation of L_3, 1 mark for setting the equations for L_2 and L_3 equal to each other and solving to find x or y, 1 mark for the correct answer]

Pages 35-36: Harder Graphs

1 The two closest points are $(3, 3)$ and $(-3, -3)$.

Use Pythagoras to find the distance between them, d:

$d^2 = (3 - -3)^2 + (3 - -3)^2 = 6^2 + 6^2 = 72$, so $d = \sqrt{72} = 6\sqrt{2}$

[3 marks available — 1 mark for finding the two closest points, 1 mark for using Pythagoras to find the distance, 1 mark for the correct answer]

2 Use Pythagoras to find the radius, r:

$r^2 = 7^2 + 24^2 = 625$, so $r = \sqrt{625} = 25$ *[1 mark]*

The equation of a circle is given by $x^2 + y^2 = r^2$,

so the equation is $x^2 + y^2 = 625$ *[1 mark]*.

[2 marks available in total — as above]

3 Find the equation of the line that should be drawn:

$x^2 + x = 1$

$x^2 + x - 4 = -3$

$x^2 - x - 4 = -3 - 2x$

So draw the line $y = -3 - 2x$ to find the solutions *[1 mark]*:

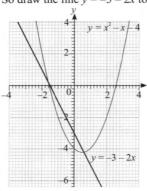

[1 mark]

So solutions to $x^2 + x = 1$ are $x \approx -1.6$ *[1 mark]* and $x \approx 0.6$ *[1 mark]*

[4 marks available in total — as above]

4 The line from the origin to the point $(-4, -3)$ is a radius, so has

gradient $\frac{0 - -3}{0 - -4} = \frac{3}{4}$, so the tangent at this point has gradient $-\frac{4}{3}$ as a tangent meets a radius at 90°.

The tangent passes through the point $(-4, -3)$, so $-3 = -\frac{4}{3}(-4) + c$

$-3 = \frac{16}{3} + c$, so $c = -\frac{25}{3}$

So the equation of the tangent at $(-4, -3)$ is $y = -\frac{4}{3}x - \frac{25}{3}$

[3 marks available — 1 mark for finding the gradient of the radius, 1 mark for finding the gradient of the tangent, 1 mark for the correct answer]

5 Substituting the coordinates of A and B into the curve $y = ab^x$

gives $36 = ab^2$ and $81 = ab^4$ *[1 mark]*

C has coordinates $(2, a(2b)^2) = (2, 4ab^2) = (2, 4 \times 36)$

$= (2, 144)$ *[1 mark]*

and D has coordinates $(4, a(2b)^4) = (4, 16ab^4) = (4, 16 \times 81)$

$= (4, 1296)$ *[1 mark]*

Gradient of $CD = \frac{1296 - 144}{4 - 2}$ *[1 mark]* $= \frac{1152}{2} = 576$ *[1 mark]*

[5 marks available in total — as above]

Pages 37-38: Trig Graphs

1 $x = 285°$ *[1 mark]*

2 Using the symmetry of the graph, $x = 90° - 15° = 75°$ *[1 mark]*

and $x = 270° - 15° = 255°$ *[1 mark]*

[2 marks available in total — as above]

3 $y = \sin 2x + 3 = \sin 2(22.5°) + 3 = \sin 45° + 3 = \frac{1}{\sqrt{2}} + 3 = \frac{\sqrt{2}}{2} + 3$

[2 marks available — 2 marks for the correct answer, otherwise 1 mark for attempting to find sin 45°]

You didn't actually need the graph for this one — it's just there to give you an idea of the shape. Don't forget to rationalise the denominator.

4 a) Using the symmetry of the graph,

$x = 180° - 55° = 125°$ *[1 mark]*

b) Extending the graph, $x = 180° + 55° = 235°$ *[1 mark]*

c) The cos graph has a line of symmetry at $x = 0$,

so $x = -55°$ *[1 mark]*

5 The two graphs intersect when $x = 45°$, so $\tan 45° = -\sin 45° + c$,

which means $c = \tan 45° + \sin 45°$ *[1 mark]*

$\tan 45° = 1$ and $\sin 45° = \frac{1}{\sqrt{2}}$, so $c = 1 + \frac{1}{\sqrt{2}}$ *[1 mark]*

So $a = -\sin 90° + 1 + \frac{1}{\sqrt{2}}$

$= -1 + 1 + \frac{1}{\sqrt{2}}$ *[1 mark]* $= \frac{1}{\sqrt{2}} = \frac{\sqrt{2}}{2}$ *[1 mark]*

[4 marks available in total — as above]

Answers

Pages 39-41: Graph Transformations

1 a)
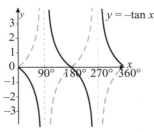
[1 mark]

b)
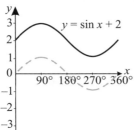
[1 mark]

2 a)
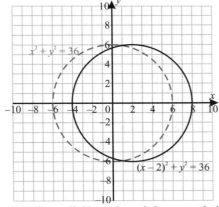
[3 marks available — 1 mark for reflecting the graph in the y-axis, 1 mark for the correct turning point, 1 mark for both correct x-intercepts]

b) Turning point = (–3 – 3, 4 + 2) = (–6, 6)
[2 marks available — 1 mark for the correct x-coordinate, 1 mark for the correct y-coordinate]

3 a)
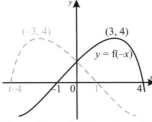
[2 marks available — 1 mark for a translation of 2 units to the right, 1 mark for the correct x-intercepts]

b) (–6, 0) *[1 mark]*

4 a)
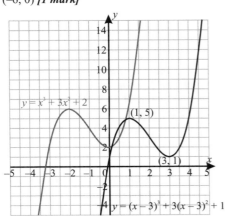
[3 marks available — 1 mark for a translation of 3 units to the right, 1 mark for a translation of 1 unit down, 1 mark for both correct turning points]

b) $(x-3)^3 = (x-3)(x-3)(x-3) = (x^2 - 6x + 9)(x - 3)$ *[1 mark]*
$= x^3 - 3x^2 - 6x^2 + 18x + 9x - 27$
$= x^3 - 9x^2 + 27x - 27$ *[1 mark]*
$(x-3)^3 + 3(x-3)^2 + 1$
$= x^3 - 9x^2 + 27x - 27 + 3(x^2 - 6x + 9) + 1$ *[1 mark]*
$= x^3 - 6x^2 + 9x + 1$ *[1 mark]*
[4 marks available in total — as above]

5 a) $5 \div 2 = \frac{5}{2}$, so the brackets are $(x - \frac{5}{2})^2$ *[1 mark]*.
Expanding the brackets: $(x - \frac{5}{2})^2 = x^2 - 5x + \frac{25}{4}$
To complete the square: $7 - \frac{25}{4} = \frac{3}{4}$ *[1 mark]*
So $x^2 + 5x + 7 = (x - \frac{5}{2})^2 + \frac{3}{4}$.
So the coordinates of the turning point are $(\frac{5}{2}, \frac{3}{4})$ *[1 mark]*
[3 marks available in total — as above]

b) Turning point = $(\frac{5}{2} - 3, \frac{3}{4} - 2) = (-\frac{1}{2}, -\frac{5}{4})$
[2 marks available — 1 mark for each correct coordinate]

c) x-intercepts are where f(x + 3) – 2 = 0
$f(x+3) - 2 = (x+3)^2 - 5(x+3) + 7 - 2 = x^2 + x - 1$ *[1 mark]*
So $x^2 + x - 1 = 0$
$x = \frac{-1 \pm \sqrt{1^2 - (4 \times 1 \times -1)}}{2 \times 1}$ *[1 mark]* $= \frac{-1 \pm \sqrt{5}}{2}$
So $x = \frac{-1 + \sqrt{5}}{2}$ or $x = \frac{-1 - \sqrt{5}}{2}$ *[1 mark for both solutions]*
[3 marks available in total — as above]
You could use the completed square form to solve the equation.

6 a) $\frac{ab}{x-a} + b = \frac{ab}{x-a} + \frac{b(x-a)}{x-a}$ *[1 mark]*
$= \frac{ab + b(x-a)}{x-a} = \frac{ab + bx - ab}{x-a} = \frac{bx}{x-a}$ *[1 mark]*
[2 marks available in total — as above]

b) From part a), $\frac{3x}{x-2} = \frac{3(2)}{x-2} + 3 = \frac{6}{x-2} + 3$ *[1 mark]*
So the transformation is a translation 2 units to the right
[1 mark] and 3 units up *[1 mark]*.
[3 marks available in total — as above]

Pages 42-44: Velocity-Time Graphs

1 Divide the area into strips of equal width, e.g.
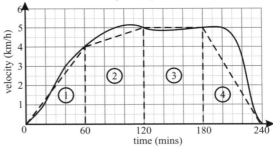
60 mins = 1 hour, so Area 1: $0.5 \times 1 \times 4 = 2$ km
Area 2: $0.5(4 + 5) \times 1 = 4.5$ km   Area 3: $5 \times 1 = 5$ km
Area 4: $0.5 \times 1 \times 5 = 2.5$ km
Total area = distance = $2 + 4.5 + 5 + 2.5 = 14$ km
[3 marks available — 1 mark for dividing the area up into strips, 1 mark for working out the area of each strip, 1 mark for a suitable answer]
You might have a different answer if you divided up the graph differently.

2 a) Divide the area into strips of equal width, e.g.
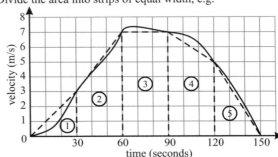

Strip 1: area = 0.5 × 30 × 3 = 45 m
Strip 2: area = 0.5(3 + 7) × 30 = 150 m
Strip 3: area = 7 × 30 = 210 m
Strip 4: area = 0.5(7 + 5) × 30 = 180 m
Strip 5: area = 0.5 × 30 × 5 = 75 m
Total area = distance = 45 + 150 + 210 + 180 + 75 = 660 m
[3 marks available — 1 mark for dividing the area up into strips, 1 mark for working out the area of each strip, 1 mark for a suitable answer]

b) E.g. the answer is likely to be an underestimate, as most of the strips go below the curve, so the strips cover a smaller area.
[2 marks available — 1 mark for a suitable answer, 1 mark for a sensible explanation]

3 Divide the area into strips of equal width, e.g.

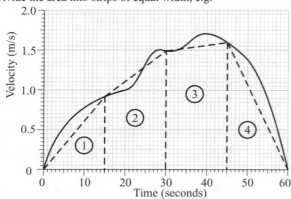

Area 1: 0.5 × 15 × 0.9 = 6.75 m
Area 2: 0.5(0.9 + 1.5) × 15 = 18 m
Area 3: 0.5(1.5 + 1.6) × 15 = 23.25 m
Area 4: 0.5 × 15 × 1.6 = 12 m
Total area = distance = 6.75 + 18 + 23.25 + 12 = 60 m
Speed = distance ÷ time = 60 ÷ 60 = 1 m/s
[4 marks available — 1 mark for dividing the area up into strips, 1 mark for working out the area of each strip, 1 mark for a suitable distance, 1 mark for dividing by the total time taken to find the speed]

4 First divide the area into six strips of equal width:

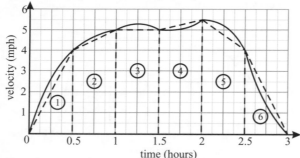

Strip 1: area = 0.5 × 0.5 × 4 = 1 mile
Strip 2: area = 0.5(4 + 5) × 0.5 = 2.25 miles
Strip 3: area = 5 × 0.5 = 2.5 miles
Strip 4: area = 0.5(5 + 5.5) × 0.5 = 2.625 miles
Strip 5: area = 0.5(5.5 + 4) × 0.5 = 2.375 miles
Strip 6: area = 0.5 × 0.5 × 4 = 1 mile
Total area = distance = 1 + 2.25 + 2.5 + 2.625 + 2.375 + 1
          = 11.75 miles

Then divide the area into three strips of equal width:

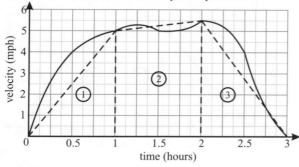

Strip 1: area = 0.5 × 1 × 5 = 2.5 miles
Strip 2: area = 0.5(5 + 5.5) × 1 = 5.25 miles
Strip 3: area = 0.5 × 1 × 5.5 = 2.75 miles
Total area = distance = 2.5 + 5.25 + 2.75 = 10.5 miles

Percentage difference = $\frac{11.75 - 10.5}{11.75} \times 100$ = 10.638... = 10.6%
[6 marks available — 1 mark for finding the area for each of the three strips, 1 mark for finding the total area using three strips, 2 marks for finding the area for each of the six strips (otherwise 1 mark for finding the area of four or five strips), 1 mark for finding the total area using six strips, 1 mark for the percentage difference]

Q5 Divide the areas into strips of equal width, e.g.

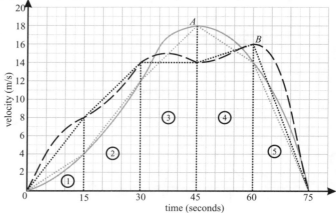

Object *A*: Strip 1: area = 0.5 × 15 × 4 = 30 m
Strip 2: area = 0.5(4 + 12) × 15 = 120 m
Strip 3: area = 0.5(12 + 18) × 15 = 225 m
Strip 4: area = 0.5(18 + 14) × 15 = 240 m
Strip 5: area = 0.5 × 15 × 14 = 105 m
Total area = distance = 30 + 120 + 225 + 240 + 105 = 720 m
Average speed = 720 ÷ 75 = 9.6 m/s
Object *B*: Strip 1: area = 0.5 × 15 × 8 = 60 m
Strip 2: area = 0.5(8 + 14) × 15 = 165 m
Strip 3: area = 14 × 15 = 210 m
Strip 4: area = 0.5(14 + 16) × 15 = 225 m
Strip 5: area = 0.5 × 15 × 16 = 120 m
Total area = distance = 60 + 165 + 210 + 225 + 120 = 780 m
Average speed = 780 ÷ 75 = 10.4 m/s
So ratio of speeds = 9.6 : 10.4 = 96 : 104 = 12 : 13
[6 marks available — 1 mark for dividing the area up into strips of equal width, 1 mark for finding the area of each strip for object A, 1 mark for finding the average speed of object A, 1 mark for find the area of each strip for object B, 1 mark for finding the average speed of object B, 1 mark for the correct answer]

Pages 45-46: Gradients

1 0800 to 1200 is 4 hours and the temperature changes by 29 − 22.5 = 6.5 °C, so the average rate of change between 8 am and 12 noon is $\frac{6.5}{4}$ = 1.625 °C/hour
1600 to 1800 is 2 hours and the temperature changes by 26.5 − 22.5 = 4 °C, so the average rate of change between 4 pm and 6 pm is $\frac{4}{2}$ = 2 °C/hour. So the manager is incorrect.
[3 marks available — 1 mark for finding the average rate of change between 8 am and 12 noon, 1 mark for finding the average rate of change between 4 pm and 6 pm, 1 mark for saying the manager is incorrect]

2 a) Gradient of line connecting (10, 15) and (20, 20)
      = average acceleration between 10 and 20 seconds
      = $\frac{20-15}{20-10} = \frac{5}{10}$ = 0.5 m/s²
      [2 marks available — 2 marks for correct answer, otherwise 1 mark for correct coordinates of the two points]

Answers

b) Draw a tangent to the graph at 50 seconds, e.g.

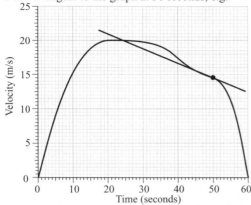

Gradient of tangent at 50 seconds = gradient of line connecting (29, 19) and (57, 13):

$\frac{13-19}{57-29} = \frac{-6}{28} = -0.21428... = -0.214$ m/s² (3 s.f.)

[2 marks available — 2 marks for the correct answer, otherwise 1 mark for correctly drawing the tangent]
It can be a bit tricky to draw the tangent exactly — as long as you got a similar answer, you'll be fine.

3 Plant A: gradient of line connecting (0, 0) and (7, 6)
= average rate of growth during the first week: $\frac{6-0}{7-0} = \frac{6}{7}$ cm/day

Plant B: gradient of line connecting (7, 4) and (14, 7)
= average rate of growth during the first week: $\frac{7-4}{14-7} = \frac{3}{7}$ cm/day

Ratio = $\frac{6}{7} : \frac{3}{7} = 6:3 = 2:1$

[3 marks available in total — 1 mark for finding the average rate of growth for plant A, 1 mark for finding the average rate of growth for plant B, 1 mark for the correct ratio]

4 a) Draw a tangent to the graph at 35 mins, e.g.

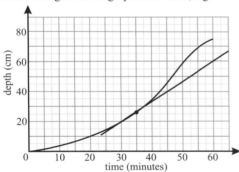

Gradient of tangent at 35 mins = gradient of line connecting (45, 40) and (60, 60): $\frac{60-40}{60-45} = \frac{20}{15} = \frac{4}{3}$ cm/min

[2 marks available — 2 marks for the correct answer, otherwise 1 mark for correctly drawing the tangent]

  b) After 60 mins, the water is 75 cm deep, so average rate = gradient of line connecting (0, 0) and (60, 75):

$= \frac{75-0}{60-0} = \frac{75}{60} = 1.25$ cm/min

[2 marks available — 2 marks for the correct answer, otherwise 1 mark for correct coordinates of the two points]

Section 4 — Ratio, Proportion and Rates of Change

Pages 47-48: Ratios

1 Speed = Distance ÷ Time
Speed of rowing boat = 18 ÷ 2.25 = 8 km/h
Speed of canoe = 15 ÷ 1.5 = 10 mph ≈ 10 × 1.6 = 16 km/h
So the ratio of the speeds is 8 km/h : 16 km/h = 1 : 2

[4 marks available — 1 mark for finding the speed of the boat, 1 mark for finding the speed of the canoe, 1 mark for a ratio with both parts in the same units, 1 mark for the correct answer]
You could have converted the rowing boat's speed into mph — just make sure both speeds have the same units before you simplify your ratio.

2 Let triangle A have height x cm and base length y cm.
Then triangle B has height x + 1 cm and base length 3y cm.
The area of triangle B is 45 cm², so the area of triangle A is (45 ÷ 9) × 2 = 10 cm².
Triangle A: $\frac{1}{2} \times x \times y = 10$ so $xy = 20$ [1]

Triangle B: $\frac{1}{2} \times (x+1) \times 3y = 45$, rearranging gives $xy + y = 30$ [2]

Substituting [1] into [2] gives: $20 + y = 30$ so $y = 10$
Put this value back into [1] to give $x = 2$.
Height of triangle A = 2 cm and height of triangle B = 2 + 1 = 3 cm.
So the ratio of vertical heights is 2 : 3.

[5 marks available — 1 mark for setting up an equation for the area of triangle A, 1 mark for setting up an equation for the area of triangle B, 1 mark for a correct method to solve the equations simultaneously, 1 mark for the correct vertical heights of each triangle, 1 mark for the correct answer]

3 E.g. Say that Jenna has completed x% and Harvey has completed y%. Then $x : y = 3 : 4$ and $x + 7 : y + 7 = 7 : 9$.
$\frac{x}{y} = \frac{3}{4}$ and $\frac{x+7}{y+7} = \frac{7}{9}$

$4x = 3y$ and $9(x+7) = 7(y+7)$
$4x - 3y = 0$ [1] and $9x - 7y = -14$ [2]
[1] × 7: $28x - 21y = 0$ [3], and [2] × 3: $27x - 21y = -42$ [4]
[3] − [4]: $x = 42$, so she has completed 42% of the game.

[4 marks available — 1 mark for setting up two ratios in terms of x and y and converting them to fractions, 1 mark for multiplying out the fractions to form a pair of simultaneous equations, 1 mark for a correct method to solve the simultaneous equations, 1 mark for the correct answer]

4 $x - 10 : y - 10 = 2 : 5$ and $x + 8 : y + 8 = 1 : 2$.
$\frac{x-10}{y-10} = \frac{2}{5}$ and $\frac{x+8}{y+8} = \frac{1}{2}$

$5(x - 10) = 2(y - 10)$ and $2(x + 8) = y + 8$
$5x - 2y = 30$ [1] and $2x - y = -8$ [2]
[2] × 2: $4x - 2y = -16$ [4]
[1] − [3]: $x = 46$
Substitute into [2] to find y: $(2 \times 46) - y = -8$ so $y = 100$

So x as a percentage of y is: $\frac{46}{100} \times 100 = 46\%$

[5 marks available — 1 mark for setting up two ratios in terms of x and y and converting them to fractions, 1 mark for multiplying out the fractions to form a pair of simultaneous equations, 1 mark for a correct method to solve the simultaneous equations, 1 mark for the correct values of x and y, 1 mark for the correct answer]

5 Let the original number of red and green sweets in the bag be x.
Let the number of yellow sweets be y.
The numbers of red, yellow and green sweets remaining are $x - 5$, $y - 15$ and $x - 25$ respectively.
red : yellow = 2 : 3 so $x - 5 : y - 15 = 2 : 3$
$\frac{x-5}{y-15} = \frac{2}{3}$

$3(x - 5) = 2(y - 15)$, so $3x - 2y = -15$ [1]

yellow : green = 3 : 1 so $y - 15 : x - 25 = 3 : 1$
$\frac{y-15}{x-25} = 3$

$y - 15 = 3(x - 25)$, so $3x - y = 60$ [2]
[2] − [1]: $y = 75$

Substituting back into [2] gives $3x - 75 = 60$, so $x = 45$
The total number of sweets originally in the bag is
$45 + 75 + 45 = 165$
The fraction that are yellow is $\frac{75}{165} = \frac{5}{11}$

[6 marks available — 1 mark for giving the number of red, yellow and green sweet in terms of x and y, 1 mark for setting up two ratios in terms of x and y and converting them to fractions, 1 mark for multiplying out the fractions to form a pair of simultaneous equations, 1 mark for a correct method to solve the simultaneous equations, 1 mark for the correct values of x and y, 1 mark for the correct answer]

Pages 49-50: Direct and Inverse Proportion

1 a) $x \propto M$, so $x = kM$ *[1 mark]*
When $M = 40$, $x = 2$
$2 = k \times 40$, so $k = 2 \div 40 = \frac{1}{20}$ *[1 mark]*
So $x = \frac{1}{20}M$ or $M = 20x$ *[1 mark]*
[3 marks available in total — as above]

   b) $x = \frac{1}{20}M$ so when $M = 55$, $x = \frac{1}{20} \times 55 = 2.75$ cm *[1 mark]*

2 a) $w \propto r^3$, so $w = kr^3$ *[1 mark]*
When $r = 6$, $w = 1080$, so $1080 = k \times 6^3$, so $k = 5$ *[1 mark]*
So $w = 5r^3$
When $w = 8640$, $5r^3 = 8640$ *[1 mark]*
$r^3 = 1728$, so $r = 12$ *[1 mark]*
[4 marks available in total — as above]

   b)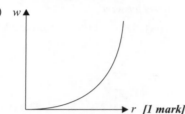
   r *[1 mark]*

3 $p \propto q$ and $q \propto \frac{1}{r}$ so $p = Aq$ and $q = \frac{B}{r}$ *[1 mark for both]*
When $p = 8$, $q = 25$ so $A = 8 \div 25 = 0.32$ *[1 mark]*
When $q = 25$, $r = 16$ so $B = 25 \times 16 = 400$ *[1 mark]*
So when $r = 2$, $q = \frac{400}{2} = 200$ *[1 mark]*
And so $p = 0.32 \times 200 = 64$ *[1 mark]*
[5 marks available in total — as above]

4 $a \propto \frac{1}{b}$ and $a \propto \frac{1}{c^2}$ so $a = \frac{M}{b}$ and $a = \frac{N}{c^2}$
Substituting for a gives: $\frac{M}{b} = \frac{N}{c^2}$ and so
$b = \frac{M}{N}c^2$ where $\frac{M}{N}$ is just a constant so $b \propto c^2$.
[3 marks available — 1 mark for writing both proportions as equations, 1 mark for substituting for a to equate the two fractions, 1 mark for rearranging into the form b = kc² where k is a constant and explaining that this is the equation of a direct proportion]

5 Let the object have density $= d_1$ and volume $= v$.
Call the object's density after the increase d_2.
Volume of the object after the increase $= 1.4v$.
$d \propto \frac{1}{v}$ so $d_1 = \frac{k}{v}$ and $d_2 = \frac{k}{1.4v}$ *[1 mark]*
k is the same in both cases as the mass of the object doesn't change.
$d_1v = k$ and $1.4d_2v = k$
$d_1v = 1.4d_2v$
$d_1 = 1.4d_2$ *[1 mark]*
So $d_2 = \frac{1}{1.4}d_1 = 0.71428...\, d_1$ *[1 mark]*
d_2 is 71.428...% of d_1, so the percentage decrease is
$100 - 71.428... = 28.571... = 28.6\%$ (1 d.p.) *[1 mark]*
[4 marks available in total — as above]

6 $y \propto \frac{1}{x^2}$ and $y \propto z^3$ so $y = \frac{A}{x^2}$ and $y = Bz^3$ *[1 mark for both]*
From the graph, when $x = 3$, $y = 80$ so $A = 80 \times 3^2 = 720$ *[1 mark]*
So when $x = 2$, $y = \frac{720}{2^2} = 180$ *[1 mark]*
When $y = 180$, $z = 5$, so $B = 180 \div 5^3 = 1.44$ *[1 mark]*
So when $z = 15$, $y = 1.44 \times 15^3 = 4860$ *[1 mark]*
[5 marks available in total — as above]

Pages 51-52: Percentages

1 1st quarter sales: £12 000 000
2nd quarter sales: £12 000 000 × 1.1 = £13 200 000
3rd quarter sales: £13 200 000 × 1.1 = £14 520 000
4th quarter sales: £14 520 000 × 1.1 = £15 972 000
Total sales = £12 000 000 + £13 200 000 + £14 520 000
+ £15 972 000 = £55 692 000

Profit = 28% of £55 692 000 = 0.28 × 55 692 000 = £15 593 760
Bonus = 30% of £15 593 760 = 0.3 × 15 593 760
= £4 678 128 = £4 700 000 (2 s.f.)
[4 marks available — 1 mark for working out the sales in the 2nd, 3rd and 4th quarters, 1 mark for working out the total yearly sales, 1 mark for working out the profit for the year, 1 mark for the correct answer]

2 Simone scored 0.85 × 120 = 102 marks on exam A, and
0.5 × 80 = 40 marks on exam B. *[1 mark for both]*
Let M be the total number of marks available on exam C,
then she scored $0.95M$ marks on exam C.
So her total number of marks was $102 + 40 + 0.95M$. *[1 mark]*
Her total number of marks was also $0.75 \times (120 + 80 + M)$
So $102 + 40 + 0.95M = 0.75(120 + 80 + M)$ *[1 mark]*
$142 + 0.95M = 150 + 0.75M$
$0.2M = 8$, so $M = 40$ *[1 mark]*
[4 marks available in total — as above]

3 Call the side length of cube $A = s$,
then side length of cube $B = 1.2s$ *[1 mark]*
Let P_A be the pressure of cube A, P_B be the pressure of cube B
and w be the weight of each cube.
Pressure $= \frac{Force}{Area}$, so $P_A = \frac{w}{s^2}$ so $w = P_As^2$ *[1 mark]*
$P_B = \frac{w}{(1.2s)^2}$ so $w = 1.44P_Bs^2$ *[1 mark]*
Equating values of w gives: $P_As^2 = 1.44P_Bs^2$, so $P_A = 1.44P_B$
So P_A is 144% of P_B *[1 mark]*
[4 marks available in total — as above]

4 Each year, 10% is added to the customer's money
and the investment company takes 12 − 10 = 2%
The customer's money at the start of each year is:
Year 1 = £100 000, Year 2 = £100 000 × 1.1 = £110 000,
Year 3 = £110 000 × 1.1 = £121 000
And the investment company makes:
Year 1 = £100 000 × 0.02 = £2000,
Year 2 = £110 000 × 0.02 = £2200,
Year 3 = £121 000 × 0.02 = £2420
So the investment company makes £2000 + £2200 + £2420 = £6620
[5 marks available — 1 mark for a correct method to find the customer's money each year, 1 mark for the correct amounts of the customer's money, 1 mark for a correct method to find the investment company's money each year, 1 mark for the correct amounts of the company's money, 1 mark for the correct answer]

5 Let the number of houses in Liverstone be L, then the number of
houses in Ashmouth is $1.7L$. *[1 mark]*
Expressions for the number of terraced houses in each village are:
Liverstone: $0.28L$ Ashmouth: $0.2 \times 1.7L$
So $(0.2 \times 1.7L) - 0.28L = 480$ *[1 mark]*
$0.34L - 0.28L = 480$
$0.06L = 480$, so $L = 8000$ *[1 mark]*
So there are 8000 houses in Liverstone, and
8000 × 1.7 = 13 600 houses in Ashmouth. *[1 mark]*
There are 8000 × 0.38 = 3040 semi-detached houses in Liverstone
and 13 600 × 0.4 = 5440 semi-detached houses in Ashmouth.
The difference in the number of semi-detached houses is
5440 − 3040 = 2400 *[1 mark]*
[5 marks available in total — as above]

Section Five — Geometry and Measures

Pages 53-55: Circle Geometry

1 E.g. By the alternate segment theorem, angle $ABC = x$ *[1 mark]*
As $AB = AC$, angle $ACB = x$ (isosceles triangle) *[1 mark]*
AB is parallel to DE, so angle $BAC = x$ (alternate angles) *[1 mark]*
All three angles inside the triangle are equal,
so ABC is an equilateral triangle. *[1 mark]*
[4 marks available in total — as above]
There's often more than one way to answer circle theorem questions — as long as you show clearly what you're doing, you'll get the marks.

2   E.g. Triangle *AOD* is isosceles,
so angle *ODA* = (180° − 128°) ÷ 2 = 26° *[1 mark]*
Triangle *BOC* is also isosceles, so angle *OBC* = 41° *[1 mark]*
ABCD is a cyclic quadrilateral, so angle *ABC* + angle *CDA* = 180°
Angle *CDA* = 180° − (59° + 41°) = 80° *[1 mark]*
Angle *CDO* = angle *CDA* − angle *ODA* = 80° − 26° = 54° *[1 mark]*
[4 marks available in total — as above]

3   E.g. Divide the triangle into two isosceles triangles,
as shown below, and label the angles *a* and *b*:

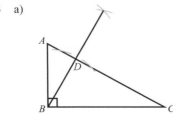

[1 mark]. Then *a* + *a* + *b* + *b* = 180° *[1 mark]*
(as the angles in a triangle add up to 180°). So 2*a* + 2*b* = 180°,
which means *a* + *b* = 90° *[1 mark]*, so the angle is a right angle.
[3 marks available in total — as above]

4   E.g. Angle *CDE* = 44° (the angle at the centre is double the angle at
the circumference) *[1 mark]*
Angle *FBC* = 76° (angles in the same segment are equal) *[1 mark]*
Angle *BFE* = 180° − 44° − 76° = 60° (angles in a triangle
add up to 180°, and *BDF* is a triangle) *[1 mark]*.
[3 marks available in total — as above]

5   E.g. By the alternate segment theorem, angle *DBC* = 54° *[1 mark]*
DB is a straight line, so angle *DXC* = 180° − 94° = 86° *[1 mark]*
If *X* was the centre of the circle, then angle *DXC* = 2 × angle *DBC*
[1 mark]. But 2 × angle *DBC* = 2 × 54° = 108° ≠ 86° *[1 mark]*,
so *X* is not the centre of the circle.
[4 marks available in total — as above]

6   E.g. Angle *AFB* = angle *ABF* (tangents from the same point
are the same length, so triangle *ABF* is isosceles)
Angle *AFB* = angle *ABF* = (180° − 36°) ÷ 2 = 72° *[1 mark]*
Angle *AFO* = 90° (tangent meets a radius at 90°),
so angle *BFO* = angle *FBO* = 90° − 72° = 18° *[1 mark]*
Angle *FEC* = 180° − 56° − 18° = 106° *[1 mark]*
(opposite angles in a cyclic quadrilateral add up to 180°)
Angle *DCE* = 180° − 112° = 68° and angle *DEC* = 180° − 106°
= 74° *[1 mark for DCE and DEC]* (angles on a straight line)
Angle *CDE* = 180° − 68° − 74° = 38° *[1 mark]*
[5 marks available in total — as above]

7   E.g. Angle *ACB* = *x*° (by the alternate segment theorem) *[1 mark]*
Angle *OCF* = 90° (tangent meets a radius at 90°) *[1 mark]*
So angle *OCA* = 90 − *y*° *[1 mark]*
a = angle *ACB* − angle *OCA* = *x* − (90° − *y*) = *x* + *y* − 90° *[1 mark]*
[4 marks available in total — as above]

Pages 56-57: Similarity and Congruence

1   Angle *BAF* = angle *BCF* *[1 mark]*
(opposite angles in a parallelogram are equal)
angle *AEB* = angle *DBC* *[1 mark]* (alternate angles)
angle *ABE* = angle *BDC* (as the other two pairs of angles match up)
All three angles match up, so the triangles are similar *[1 mark]*.
[3 marks available in total — as above]

2   The trapezium is isosceles, so side *AD* = side *BC* *[1 mark]*.
Angles in the same segment are equal, so angle *DAX* = angle *CBX*
and angle *ADX* = angle *BCX* *[1 mark for both angle pairs]*.
The condition AAS holds, so triangles *AXD* and *BXC*
are congruent *[1 mark]*.
[3 marks available in total — as above]

3   a)

*[2 marks available — 1 mark for a correct method,
1 mark for the correct line drawn]*

b) Angle *ADB* = angle *CDB* = 90° (as *BD* is perpendicular to *AC*)
angle *DCB* + angle *CBD* = 90° (angles in a triangle),
angle *ABD* + angle *DAB* = 90° (angles in a triangle)
and angle *ABD* + angle *CBD* = 90° (angles in a right angle)
So angle *DCB* = angle *ABD* and angle *DAB* = angle *CBD*
All three angles match up, so the triangles are similar.
*[3 marks available — 1 mark for stating that angle ADB =
angle CDB, 1 mark for showing that another pair of angles
are equal, 1 mark for showing that the final pair of angles are
equal and stating that this means the triangles are similar]*

4   Opposite angles in a parallelogram are equal,
so angle *MAQ* = angle *NCP* *[1 mark]*.
Opposite sides of a parallelogram are equal, and *M* and *P*
are the midpoints of *AB* and *CD* respectively,
so side *AM* = side *CP* *[1 mark]*.
Opposite sides of a parallelogram are equal, and *N* and *Q*
are the midpoints of *BC* and *DA* respectively,
so side *AQ* = side *NC* *[1 mark]*.
The condition SAS holds, so triangles *AMP* and *PNC*
are congruent *[1 mark]*.
[4 marks available in total — as above]

5   The *y*-axis and the line L_3 are parallel, so angle *RQP* = angle *NMP*
[1 mark] and angle *QRP* = angle *MNP* *[1 mark]* (alternate angles).
Find the lengths of *NP* and *PR*:
Putting *x* = 0 and *y* = 0 into the equation for line L_2 gives the
coordinates *N*(0, 5) and *R*(4, 0) *[1 mark for both points]*.
Find the lengths of sides *NP* and *PR*:
$NP^2 = (2 − 0)^2 + (2.5 − 5)^2 = 4 + 6.25 = 10.25$
So $NP = \sqrt{10.25}$ *[1 mark]*
$PR^2 = (4 − 2)^2 + (2.5 − 0)^2 = 4 + 6.25 = 10.25$
So $PR = \sqrt{10.25}$
So *NP* = *PR* *[1 mark]*
The condition AAS holds, so triangles *MNP* and *QRP*
are congruent *[1 mark]*.
[6 marks available in total — as above]

6   Prove that triangles *AOM* and *BOM* are congruent:
OM is common to both triangles.
Angles *OMA* = *OMB* = 90° and *OB* = *OA* (both are a radius)
The condition RHS holds, so triangles *AOM* and *BOM*
are congruent. Therefore *AM* = *MB* so *OP* bisects the chord.
*[4 marks available — 1 mark for any statement of congruence,
1 mark for the other two statements of congruence, 1 mark for
RHS, 1 mark for stating that AM = MB]*

Pages 58-59: Arcs, Sectors and Segments

1   Area = $\frac{x}{360} \times 12^2 \times \pi$
$88\pi = \frac{144\pi x}{360} = \frac{2\pi x}{5}$
$x = 88 \times \frac{5}{2} = 220°$

*[3 marks available — 1 mark for a correct formula for the area of
a sector, 1 mark for substituting in the numbers correctly, 1 mark
for the correct value of x]*

2   a)   Area of sector = $\frac{70}{360} \times 6^2 \times \pi = 7\pi$ cm²
Area of triangle = ½ × 6² × sin 70° = 16.914... cm²
Area of segment = 7π − 16.914... = 5.076... = 5.08 cm² (3 s.f.)
*[3 marks available — 1 mark for finding the area of the
sector, 1 mark for finding the area of the triangle, 1 mark for
the correct answer]*

b)   Perimeter of segment = arc + chord
Arc length = $\frac{70}{360} \times 2 \times \pi \times 6 = \frac{7}{3}\pi$ cm
To find the chord length, use the cosine rule:
$a^2 = 6^2 + 6^2 − (2 × 6 × 6 × \cos 70°) = 47.374...$
a = 6.882... cm
Perimeter = $\frac{7}{3}\pi$ + 6.882... = 14.213... = 14.2 cm (3 s.f.)
*[4 marks available — 1 mark for the arc length, 1 mark for
putting the numbers into the cosine rule formula correctly,
1 mark for the chord length, 1 mark for the correct answer]*

3   Arc length = 21.6 – 8 – 8 = 5.6 cm *[1 mark]*
    Circumference = 2 × 8 × π = 50.265... cm *[1 mark]*
    50.265... ÷ 5.6 = 8.975... ≈ 9 sectors in total *[1 mark]*
    [3 marks available in total — as above]
    Don't forget to round your answer — there'll be a whole number of sectors (and the original perimeter was rounded as well).

4   a)   Area of segment with radius 8 cm = $(\frac{45}{360} × 8^2 × π)$
                                          = $8π$ cm^2 *[1 mark]*

         Area of segment with radius 5 cm = $(\frac{45}{360} × 5^2 × π)$
                                          = $\frac{25}{8}π$ cm^2 *[1 mark]*

         Area of white icing = $8π - \frac{25}{8}π$ = 15.315...
                             = 15.3 cm^2 (3 s.f.) *[1 mark]*
         [3 marks available in total — as above]
         It's always a good idea to leave your working in terms of π for as long as possible — it means you don't lose any accuracy later on.

    b)   Area of top of slice = $\frac{45}{360}$ × 10^2 × π = 12.5π cm^2 *[1 mark]*
         Volume of slice = 12.5π × 8 = 100π = 314.159...
                         = 314 cm^3 (3 s.f.) *[1 mark]*
         [2 marks available in total — as above]

5   a)   Angle DFC = (360° – 140°) ÷ 2 = 110°
         and angle DCF = 60° ÷ 2 = 30° *[1 mark for both]*
         Using the sine rule, $\frac{DC}{\sin 110°} = \frac{1.6}{\sin 30°}$ *[1 mark]*

         So DC = sin 110° × $\frac{1.6}{\sin 30°}$ = 3.0070...
                = 3.01 cm (3 s.f.) *[1 mark]*
         [3 marks available in total — as above]
         There are other ways of answering this question — but you should still find that DC = 3.01 cm to 3 s.f.

    b)   From a), AD = 3.007... cm and AC = 6.014... cm
         (as D is the midpoint of AC).
         The diagram has a vertical line of symmetry, so BE = AD.
         Arc length AB = $\frac{60}{360}$ × 2 × π × 6.014... = 6.297... cm
         Arc length DE = $\frac{140}{360}$ × 2 × π × 1.6 = 3.909... cm
         Perimeter = 3.007... + 3.007... + 6.297... + 3.909...
                   = 16.221... = 16.2 cm (3 s.f.)
         [5 marks available — 1 mark for finding AC, 1 mark for the correct lengths of AD and BE, 1 mark for the correct arc length AB, 1 mark for the correct arc length DE, 1 mark for the correct answer]

Pages 60-62: 3D Shapes — Surface Area and Volume

1   Area of cross-section = ½ab sin C = ½ × 4 × 2 × sin 67°
                          = 3.682... cm^2
    Volume of prism = 3.682... × 9 = 33.138... = 33.1 cm^3 (3 s.f.)
    [3 marks available — 1 mark for putting the numbers into the area formula correctly, 1 mark for the correct cross-sectional area, 1 mark for the correct answer]

2   Volume = $\frac{1}{3}πr^2h$, so $(3.2 × 10^{26})π = \frac{1}{3} × π × (4 × 10^8)^2 × x$
    $(3.2 × 10^{26})π = \frac{1}{3} × π × 16 × 10^{16} × x$
    $9.6 × 10^{26} = (1.6 × 10^{17})x$
    $\frac{9.6}{1.6} × \frac{10^{26}}{10^{17}} = x$, so x = 6 × 10^9 m
    [3 marks available — 1 mark for squaring (4 × 10^8) correctly, 1 mark for a correct method for solving the equation, 1 mark for the correct answer]

3   Let V_A = volume of sphere A, V_B = volume of sphere B and R_B = radius of sphere B. Then
    $V_A = \frac{4}{3} × π × 6^3$ = 288π cm^3 *[1 mark]*
    V_B = 1.6 × V_A = 1.6 × 288π = 460.8π cm^3 *[1 mark]*
    R_B^3 = 460.8π ÷ $\frac{4}{3}$ ÷ π = 345.6 *[1 mark]*
    So $R_B = \sqrt[3]{345.6}$ = 7.017... = 7.02 cm (3 s.f.) *[1 mark]*
    [4 marks available in total — as above]

4   a)   The removed cone is similar and is one-third of the height of the original cone, so has radius 5 cm and height 12 cm *[1 mark]*
         Volume of frustum
         = $(\frac{1}{3} × π × 15^2 × 36) - (\frac{1}{3} × π × 5^2 × 12)$ *[1 mark]*
         = 2700π – 100π = 2600π cm^3 *[1 mark]*
         [3 marks available in total — as above]

    b)   Use Pythagoras to find the slant height, l, of the original cone:
         $l^2 = 36^2 + 15^2 = 1521$, so $l = \sqrt{1521}$ = 39 cm *[1 mark]*
         Slant height of removed cone = 39 ÷ 3 = 13 cm.
         Surface area of frustum = curved area of original cone – curved area of removed cone + both circular faces
         = (π × 15 × 39) – (π × 5 × 13) + (π × 15^2) + (π × 5^2) *[1 mark]*
         = 585π – 65π + 225π + 25π = 770π cm^2 *[1 mark]*
         [3 marks available in total — as above]

5   Volume of cylinder = π × 10^2 × 21 = 2100π cm^3 *[1 mark]*
    Volume of cone = $\frac{1}{3}$ × π × 10^2 × 21 = 700π cm^3 *[1 mark]*
    Volume not taken up by the cone = 2100π – 700π
    = 1400π cm^3 *[1 mark]* = 0.0014π m^3 *[1 mark]*
    Density = mass ÷ volume, so mass = density × volume
    mass = 0.52 × 0.0014π = 0.002287... kg *[1 mark]*
                          = 2.287... g = 2.29 g (3 s.f.) *[1 mark]*
    [6 marks available in total — as above]
    Be careful with the units here — you're given the dimensions of the shape in cm, but the density in kg/m^3. It doesn't matter when you do the unit conversions, as long as you end up with an answer in g.

6   Surface area of cylinder = 2πrh + 2πr^2 = 12πr + 2πr^2 *[1 mark]*
    Surface area of cone = πrl + πr^2 = 7πr + πr^2 *[1 mark]*
    Combined surface area = 12πr + 2πr^2 + 7πr + πr^2
                          = 19πr + 3πr^2 *[1 mark]*
    So 110π = 19πr + 3πr^2, so 3r^2 + 19r – 110 = 0 *[1 mark]*
    (3r – 11)(r + 10) = 0 *[1 mark]*, so r = $\frac{11}{3}$ or r = –10
    The radius must be positive, so r = $\frac{11}{3}$ cm *[1 mark]*
    [6 marks available in total — as above]

7   Weight of one piece = 5000 ÷ 8 = 625 N *[1 mark]*
    Area of flat face = πr^2 ÷ 4 = π × 1.4^2 ÷ 4 = 0.49π m^2 *[1 mark]*
    Pressure = force ÷ area = 625 ÷ 0.49π *[1 mark]* = 406.007...
                            = 406 N/m^2 (3 s.f.) *[1 mark]*
    [4 marks available in total — as above]

8   The slant length, l, of the cone is:
    $\sqrt{(3k)^2 + (4k^2)} = \sqrt{9k^2 + 16k^2} = \sqrt{25k^2}$ = 5k cm *[1 mark]*
    Curved surface area of cone = π × 3k × 5k = 15k^{2}π *[1 mark]*
    Curved surface area of hemisphere = 0.5 × 4π(3k)^2 = 18k^{2}π *[1 mark]*
    The total surface area of the object is
    15k^{2}π + 18k^{2}π = 33k^{2}π *[1 mark]*
    So 33k^{2}π = 3993π *[1 mark]*, so k^2 =121, so k = 11 *[1 mark]*
    [6 marks available in total — as above]

9   Volume of one sphere = (30% of 1200) ÷ 2 = 180 cm^3
    $\frac{4}{3}πr^3$ = 180 *[1 mark]* so r^3 = 42.971..., so r = 3.502... cm *[1 mark]*
    Volume of one cone = (1200 ÷ 3) ÷ 4 = 100 cm^3, so $\frac{1}{3}πr^2h$ = 100
    r = 3.502... cm, so $\frac{1}{3}$π(3.502...)^{2}h = 100 *[1 mark]*
    h = 7.783... cm *[1 mark]*
    Volume of cube = (7.783...)^3 = 471.570... cm^3 *[1 mark]*
    Amount of steel left = 1200 – 360 – 400 = 440 cm^3
    so she does not have enough steel left *[1 mark]*
    [6 marks available in total — as above]

Pages 63-64: Rates of Flow

1   Volume of tank = π × 1.6^2 × 4.5 = 11.52π m^3 *[1 mark]*
    = 11.52π × 1000 = 11 520π litres *[1 mark]*
    Rate of flow = volume ÷ time = 11 520π ÷ 25 *[1 mark]*
    = 460.8π = 1447.645... = 1450 litres per minute (3 s.f.) *[1 mark]*
    [4 marks available in total — as above]
    To convert m^3 to litres, you can first convert it to cm^3 (by multiplying by 100 × 100 × 100) then divide it by 1000 (as 1 litre = 1000 cm^3), or you can multiply by 1000 to do it all in one go.

Answers

2 a) The volume of liquid when it is 2 cm deep is the volume of a frustum formed by removing the top 6 cm of the cone.
$6 \div 8 = 0.75$, so the removed cone has a radius of
$2 \times 0.75 = 1.5$ cm *[1 mark]*.
Volume of frustum
$= (\frac{1}{3}\pi \times 2^2 \times 8) - (\frac{1}{3}\pi \times 1.5^2 \times 6) = 19.373...$ cm³ *[1 mark]*
Time taken to fill = volume ÷ rate of flow = $19.373... \div 0.5$
$= 38.746... = 38.7$ s (3 s.f.) *[1 mark]*
[3 marks available in total — as above]

b) Volume of cone $= \frac{1}{3}\pi \times 2^2 \times 8 = 33.510...$ cm³
So 89.5% of total volume $= 33.510... \times 0.895 = 29.991...$ cm³
Time taken to fill = volume ÷ rate of flow = $29.991... \div 0.5$
$= 59.9733... = 60$ s (2 s.f.)
[2 marks available — 1 mark for finding 89.5% of the volume, 1 mark for finding the time taken to fill this volume]

3 a) Cross-sectional area = ½ab sin C = ½ × $2\sqrt{3}$ × 4 × sin 60°
$= \frac{1}{2} \times 2\sqrt{3} \times 4 \times \frac{\sqrt{3}}{2} = 6$ m²
[2 marks available — 1 mark for putting the numbers into the area formula correctly, 1 mark for the correct answer]

b) Rate of flow = 90 000 litres per minute
$= 90\,000 \div 60 = 1500$ litres per second *[1 mark]*
$= 1\,500\,000$ cm³/s $= 1.5$ m³/s *[1 mark]*
Speed = rate of flow ÷ cross-sectional area of water
$= 1.5 \div 6$ *[1 mark]* $= 0.25$ m/s *[1 mark]*
[4 marks available in total — as above]

4 Volume of cone $= \frac{1}{3}\pi \times 30^2 \times 70 = 21\,000\pi$ cm³ *[1 mark]*
Volume of cylinder $= \pi \times 30^2 \times 60 = 54\,000\pi$ cm³ *[1 mark]*
Total volume $= 21\,000\pi + 54\,000\pi = 75\,000\pi$ cm³
$= 75\pi$ litres *[1 mark]*

2 minutes = 120 seconds, and time taken = volume ÷ rate of flow, so time taken to empty – time taken to fill = 120 s:
$\frac{75\pi}{(x-2)\pi} - \frac{75\pi}{x\pi} = 120$ *[1 mark]*
$75x - 75(x-2) = 120x(x-2)$
$120x^2 - 240x - 150 = 0$ *[1 mark]*
$4x^2 - 8x - 5 = 0$
$(2x + 1)(2x - 5) = 0$ *[1 mark]*
So $x = -0.5$ or $x = 2.5$, so $x = 2.5$ *[1 mark]* (as it must be positive).
[7 marks available in total — as above]

Pages 65-67: Enlargement

1 a) Ratio of surface areas $= 1^2 : 3^2 : 5^2 = 1 : 9 : 25$ *[1 mark]*

b) Height of large cylinder $= 6 \times 5 = 30$ cm
Find the radius of the large cylinder: $6750\pi = \pi \times r^2 \times 30$
So $r^2 = 6750 \div 30 = 225$, which means $r = 15$ cm
Radius of small cylinder $= 15 \div 5 = 3$ cm,
so radius of middle cylinder $= 3 \times 3 = 9$ cm
[3 marks available — 1 mark for finding the radius of the large cylinder, 1 mark for finding the radius of the small cylinder, 1 mark for the correct answer]

2 a) (Scale factor)³ $= \frac{160}{2.5 \times 10^6}$ *[1 mark]* $= \frac{1}{15\,625}$,
so scale factor $= \frac{1}{25}$ *[1 mark]*
[2 marks available in total — as above]

b) Surface area of original $= 200 \times 25^2 = 125\,000 = 1.25 \times 10^5$ m²
[2 marks available — 1 mark for correct working, 1 mark for the correct answer in standard form]

3 a) Scale factor $= \sqrt[3]{\frac{768\pi}{324\pi}} = \sqrt[3]{\frac{64}{27}} = \frac{4}{3}$ *[1 mark]*
Surface area of cone B $= 216\pi \times \left(\frac{4}{3}\right)^2 = 384\pi$ cm² *[1 mark]*
[2 marks available in total — as above]

b) $3 : 4$ *[1 mark]*

4 a) Volume of cuboid A $= 1.5 \times 2.5 \times 5 = 18.75$ cm³
Volume of cuboid B $= 18.75 \times \left(\frac{8}{5}\right)^3 = 76.8$ cm³
[2 marks available — 1 mark for a correct method, 1 mark for the correct answer]

You could have worked out the side lengths of cuboid B and multiplied them together to find the volume.

b) Density = mass ÷ volume and 0.06 kg = 60 g
Cuboid A: density = $60 \div 18.75 = 3.2$ g/cm³
Cuboid B: density = $60 \div 76.8 = 0.78125$ g/cm³
% decrease $= \frac{3.2 - 0.78125}{3.2} \times 100 = 75.585... = 75.6\%$ (3 s.f.)
[3 marks available — 1 mark for finding the density of cuboid A, 1 mark for finding the density of cuboid B, 1 mark for the correct answer]

5 Height: scale factor from small vase to medium vase
$= \sqrt{\frac{160}{90}} = \sqrt{\frac{16}{9}} = \frac{4}{3}$ *[1 mark]*
So height of small vase $= 20 \div \frac{4}{3} = 15$ cm *[1 mark]*
Volume: scale factor from small vase to large vase
$= \sqrt{\frac{1440}{90}} = \sqrt{16} = 4$ *[1 mark]*
Volume of large vase = 0.016 m³ = 16 000 cm³
So volume of small vase $= 16\,000 \div 4^3 = 250$ cm³ *[1 mark]*
[4 marks available in total — as above]

6 Scale factor $= \sqrt[3]{8.1 \div 2.4} = \sqrt[3]{3.375} = 1.5$ *[1 mark]*
Time taken to decorate large bead $= 8 \times 1.5^2 = 18$ mins *[1 mark]*
Time taken to decorate 5 small beads and 4 large beads
$= (5 \times 8) + (4 \times 18) = 112$ mins *[1 mark]*
$1\frac{3}{4}$ hours = 105 mins so Anna does not have enough time to decorate all the beads *[1 mark]*.
[4 marks available in total — as above]

Section Six — Pythagoras and Trigonometry

Pages 68-69: Trigonometry

1 The missing angle in triangle P is $180° - 90° - 30° = 60°$
The missing angle in triangle Q is $180° - 90° - 60° = 30°$
[1 mark for both missing angles]
So both triangles have angles of 60°, 30° and 90° *[1 mark]*
Hypotenuse of P = 9.7 cm
Hypotenuse of Q $= \frac{4.85}{\cos 60°}$ *[1 mark]* $= \frac{4.85}{0.5} = 9.7$ cm.
Condition AAS holds so triangles P and Q are congruent *[1 mark]*.
[4 marks available in total — as above]
You can use any of the conditions SSS, AAS, SAS or RHS to prove congruence — if you show full working, you'll get full marks.

2 The large rhombus has the following dimensions:

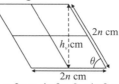

$h_v = 2n \times \sin\theta = 2n\sin\theta$ cm
Area of rhombus $= 2n \times 2n\sin\theta = 4n^2\sin\theta$ cm²
[3 marks available — 1 mark for a correct method to work out the height of the large or small rhombus, 1 mark for the correct height, 1 mark for multiplying height by base length to get $4n^2\sin\theta$ cm²]
You could also work out the area of one small rhombus then multiply it by 4 to get the area of the large rhombus.

3 Diagonals of a kite meet at right angles. So $FMG = 90°$.
$FM = \frac{9}{\tan 58°} = 5.623...$ cm *[1 mark]*
Angle $FEM = \tan^{-1}\left(\frac{5.623...}{5}\right) = 48.360...°$ *[1 mark]*
Angle HEM = angle $FEM = 48.360...°$
So angle $FEH = 48.360...° + 48.360...° = 96.721...°$
$= 96.7°$ (1 d.p.) *[1 mark]*
[3 marks available in total — as above]

4 $BC^2 = 11^2 - 7^2 = 72$ so $BC = \sqrt{72} = 6\sqrt{2}$ *[1 mark]*
$BD = \frac{6\sqrt{2}}{\cos 30°} = \frac{6\sqrt{2}}{(\sqrt{3}/2)}$ *[1 mark]*
$= \frac{2 \times 6\sqrt{2}}{\sqrt{3}} = \frac{12\sqrt{2}}{\sqrt{3}} = \frac{12\sqrt{2}\sqrt{3}}{3} = 4\sqrt{6}$ *[1 mark]*

So the radius of the semicircle = $4\sqrt{6} \div 2 = 2\sqrt{6}$ cm *[1 mark]*

So the area of the semicircle = $\dfrac{\pi \times (2\sqrt{6})^2}{2}$

$$= \dfrac{24\pi}{2} = 12\pi \text{ cm}^2 \text{ [1 mark]}$$

[5 marks available in total — as above]

5 a) Angle $ECA = 90°$ as a tangent meets a radius at $90°$.

$AC = 4 \times \tan 58° = 6.401...$ cm *[1 mark]*

So the radius of the circle is $6.401... \div 2 = 3.200...$ cm *[1 mark]*

Area of the circle = $\pi \times 3.200...^2 = 32.183...$

$$= 32.18 \text{ cm}^2 \text{ (2 d.p.) [1 mark]}$$

[3 marks available in total — as above]

b) Angle $ABC = 90°$ and angle $CAB = 180° - 90° - 58° = 32°$

$AB = 6.401... \times \cos 32° = 5.428...$ cm

$BC = 6.401... \times \sin 32° = 3.392...$ cm *[1 mark for both]*

Area of triangle $ABC = 0.5 \times 5.428... \times 3.392...$

$$= 9.207... \text{ cm}^2 \text{ [1 mark]}$$

Angle $ADC = 90°$

$AD = 6.401... \times \cos 53° = 3.852...$ cm

$DC = 6.401... \times \sin 53° = 5.112...$ cm *[1 mark for both]*

Area of triangle $ADC = 0.5 \times 3.852... \times 5.112...$

$$= 9.847... \text{ cm}^2 \text{ [1 mark]}$$

Shaded area = $32.183... - 9.207... - 9.847...$

$$= 13.128... = 13.13 \text{ cm}^2 \text{ (2 d.p.) [1 mark]}$$

[5 marks available in total — as above]

There are other angles you can use to get the side lengths of the triangles but they will all give the same answer.

Pages 70-72: The Sine and Cosine Rules

1 Using the cosine rule,

$$\cos x = \dfrac{a^2 + c^2 - b^2}{2ac} = \dfrac{(4\sqrt{2})^2 + (\sqrt{6})^2 - (\sqrt{14})^2}{2 \times 4\sqrt{2} \times \sqrt{6}} = \dfrac{32 + 6 - 14}{8\sqrt{12}}$$

$$= \dfrac{24}{8\sqrt{12}} = \dfrac{3}{\sqrt{12}} = \dfrac{3}{2\sqrt{3}} = \dfrac{3\sqrt{3}}{2\sqrt{3}\sqrt{3}} = \dfrac{3\sqrt{3}}{6} = \dfrac{\sqrt{3}}{2}$$

So $\cos x = \dfrac{\sqrt{3}}{2}$, which means that $x = 30°$

[4 marks available — 1 mark for substituting the numbers into the cosine rule formula correctly, 1 mark for simplifying the expression for cos x, 1 mark for rationalising denominator, 1 mark for showing that x = 30°]

2 Using the sine rule: $\dfrac{BD}{\sin 30°} = \dfrac{8}{\sin 70°}$ *[1 mark]*

$BD = \dfrac{8}{\sin 70°} \times \sin 30° = 4.256...$ m *[1 mark]*

$\dfrac{4}{\sin BDC} = \dfrac{4.256...}{\sin 60°}$ *[1 mark]*

$\sin BDC = \dfrac{\sin 60°}{4.256...} \times 4 = 0.813...$ *[1 mark]*

Angle $BDC = \sin^{-1}(0.813...) = 54.468...° = 54.5°$ (3 s.f.) *[1 mark]*

[5 marks available in total — as above]

3 Use the cosine rule to find the missing side of triangle DEF:

$EF^2 = (3\sqrt{2})^2 + 9^2 - (2 \times 3\sqrt{2} \times 9 \times \cos 45°)$ *[1 mark]*

$= 18 + 81 - (54\sqrt{2} \times \dfrac{1}{\sqrt{2}}) = 45$ *[1 mark]*

$EF = \sqrt{45} = 3\sqrt{5}$ cm *[1 mark]*

The sides are proportional — all the sides in triangle ABC are $\sqrt{5}$ times longer than the equivalent sides in triangle FDE (e.g. $9 \times \sqrt{5} = 9\sqrt{5}$) so they are similar. *[1 mark]*

[4 marks available in total — as above]

4 Start by working out the radius, r, of the circle:

angle $ODC =$ angle $OCD = (180° - 74°) \div 2 = 53°$

$\dfrac{r}{\sin 53°} = \dfrac{18}{\sin 74°}$, so $r = \dfrac{18}{\sin 74°} \times \sin 53° = 14.954...$ cm

Area $X = \dfrac{26}{360} \times \pi \times 14.954...^2 = 50.743...$ cm^2

Area of triangle $ODC = \dfrac{1}{2} \times 14.954... \times 14.954... \times \sin 74°$

$$= 107.490... \text{ cm}^2$$

Area $Y = \dfrac{74}{360} \times \pi \times 14.954...^2 - 107.490... = 36.932...$ cm^2

So area X is bigger.

[6 marks available — 1 mark for working out angle ODC or OCD, 1 mark for substituting the numbers into the sine rule correctly, 1 mark for the correct radius of the circle, 1 mark for working out area X, 1 mark for working out the area of triangle ODC, 1 mark for working out area Y with a correct answer]

5 Use the cosine rule to find BD and EB

$BD^2 = 15^2 + 12^2 - 2 \times 15 \times 12 \times \cos 77° = 288.017...$

So $BD = 16.971...$ cm

$EB^2 = 14^2 + 11^2 - 2 \times 14 \times 11 \times \cos 73° = 226.949...$

So $EB = 15.064...$ cm

Use the sine rule to find angle DBC and angle ABE:

$\dfrac{16.971...}{\sin 77°} = \dfrac{12}{\sin DBC}$, so $\sin DBC = \dfrac{12 \times \sin 77°}{16.971...} = 0.688...$

So angle $DBC = \sin^{-1}(0.688...) = 43.548...°$

$\dfrac{15.064...}{\sin 73°} = \dfrac{14}{\sin ABE}$, so $\sin ABE = \dfrac{14 \times \sin 73°}{15.064...} = 0.888...$

So angle $ABE = \sin^{-1}(0.888...) = 62.711...°$

Angle $EBD = 129° - 43.548...° - 62.711...° = 22.740...°$

Area $BED = \dfrac{1}{2} \times 16.971... \times 15.064... \times \sin 22.740...°$

$$= 49.414... = 49.4 \text{ cm}^2 \text{ (3 s.f.)}$$

[5 marks available — 1 mark for finding BD, 1 mark for finding EB, 1 mark for finding angle DBC, 1 mark for finding angle ABE, 1 mark for the correct answer]

You could have found angles DBC and ABE using the cosine rule.

6 $AB = x$ cm and $AB:BC = 1:2$, so $BC = 2x$ cm

So $\dfrac{1}{2} \times x \times 2x \times \sin 50° = 38$ *[1 mark]*

$x^2 = \dfrac{38}{\sin 50°} = 49.605...$, so $x = 7.043...$ *[1 mark]*

So $AB = 7.043...$ cm and $BC = 7.043 \times 2 = 14.086...$ cm

Use the cosine rule to find AC:

$AC^2 = 7.043...^2 + 14.086...^2 - 2 \times 7.043... \times 14.086... \times \cos 50°$

$= 120.484...$, so $AC = 10.976... = 11.0$ cm (3 s.f.)

[4 marks available — 1 mark for setting up an equation for the area of the triangle, 1 mark for finding the length of AB, 1 mark for a correct method to find side AC, 1 mark for the correct answer]

7 Angle $CAO =$ angle $CBO = 90°$

So angle $ACB = 360° - 118° - 90° - 90° = 62°$

Angle $CAB =$ angle $CBA = (180° - 62°) \div 2 = 59°$

Using the cosine rule to find BA:

$BA^2 = 8.5^2 + 8.5^2 - 2 \times 8.5 \times 8.5 \times \cos 118° = 212.338...$

So $BA = 14.571...$ cm

Use the sine rule to find CA: $\dfrac{CA}{\sin 59°} = \dfrac{14.571...}{\sin 62°}$

$CA = \sin 59° \times \dfrac{14.571...}{\sin 62°} = 14.146...$ cm

So area of triangle $ABC = \dfrac{1}{2} \times 14.571... \times 14.146... \times \sin 59°$

$$= 88.347... \text{ cm}^2$$

Area of triangle $OAB = \dfrac{1}{2} \times 8.5 \times 8.5 \times \sin 118° = 31.896...$ cm^2

So area of minor segment = $\left(\dfrac{118}{360} \times \pi \times 8.5^2\right) - 31.896...$

$$= 42.502... \text{ cm}^2$$

Subtract the area of the minor segment from the area of triangle ABC: $88.347... - 42.502... = 45.845... = 45.8$ cm^2 (3 s.f.)

[7 marks available — 1 mark for finding angles ACB and CAB/CBA, 1 mark for finding the length of BA, 1 mark for finding CA or CB, 1 mark for finding the area of triangle ABC, 1 mark for working out the area of triangle OAB, 1 mark for finding the area of the minor segment, 1 mark for the correct answer]

Pages 73-75: 3D Pythagoras and Trigonometry

1 The vertical height of each cone is 6 m $\div 2 = 3$ m

Let the radius of the cones be r, then, using Pythagoras:

$r^2 = 4.2^2 - 3^2 = 8.64$ so $r = 2.939...$ m *[1 mark]*

Volume of one cone = $\dfrac{1}{3} \times \pi \times 2.939...^2 \times 3$

$$= 27.143... \text{ m}^3 \text{ [1 mark]}$$

Volume of the whole solid = $27.143... \times 2$

$$= 54.286... = 54.3 \text{ m}^3 \text{ (3 s.f.) [1 mark]}$$

[3 marks available in total — as above]

2   $BA = 2\sqrt{3} \times \tan 30° = 2\sqrt{3} \times \dfrac{1}{\sqrt{3}} = 2$ cm *[1 mark]*

So the area of the triangular face $= \dfrac{1}{2} \times 2\sqrt{3} \times 2$

$\qquad\qquad\qquad\qquad\qquad\qquad = 2\sqrt{3}$ *[1 mark]*

$BC = \sqrt{2^2 + (2\sqrt{3})^2} = \sqrt{4 + 12} = \sqrt{16} = 4$ cm *[1 mark]*

So the length of the prism is $32 \div 4 = 8$ cm

Volume of the prism $= 2\sqrt{3} \times 8 = 16\sqrt{3}$ cm³ *[1 mark]*

[4 marks available — 1 mark for a correct method to find the area of the triangular face, 1 mark for the correct area of the triangular face, 1 mark for the correct length of BC, 1 mark for the correct answer]

3   Using Pythagoras' theorem on triangle AXV:

$AX^2 = 8.9^2 - 7.2^2 = 27.37$, so $AX = \sqrt{27.37}$ *[1 mark]*

and $AC = 2\sqrt{27.37}$ *[1 mark]*

Now using Pythagoras' theorem on triangle ABC:

$AB^2 = (2\sqrt{27.37})^2 - 4.2^2 = 91.84$ *[1 mark]*,

so $AB = \sqrt{91.84} = 9.583... = 9.58$ cm (3 s.f.) *[1 mark]*

[4 marks available in total — as above]

4   $XE = 8$ cm as the hexagon is made from equilateral triangles.

Let Y be the midpoint of ED, then EXY is a right-angled triangle.

$XY^2 = 8^2 - 4^2 = 48$, so $XY = \sqrt{48}$ cm *[1 mark]*

The angle between planes VED and $ABCDEF$ is angle VYX.

$\tan VYX = \dfrac{15}{\sqrt{48}}$ *[1 mark]*, so $VYX = \tan^{-1}\left(\dfrac{15}{\sqrt{48}}\right)$

$VYX = 65.208... = 65.2°$ (1 d.p.) *[1 mark]*

[3 marks available in total — as above]

5   a)   The required angle is angle HBE

$BE^2 = 5^2 + 5^2 = 50$, so $BE = \sqrt{50}$ *[1 mark]*

$\tan HBE = \dfrac{7}{\sqrt{50}}$ *[1 mark]*

So $HBE = \tan^{-1}\left(\dfrac{7}{\sqrt{50}}\right) = 44.710...° = 44.7°$ (3 s.f.) *[1 mark]*

[3 marks available in total — as above]

You could have found length HB instead of BE.

b) $MN^2 = 7^2 + 5^2 = 74$, so $MN = \sqrt{74}$ *[1 mark]*

Then BMN is a right-angled triangle.

$\tan BMN = \dfrac{2.5}{\sqrt{74}}$ *[1 mark]*

So $BMN = \tan^{-1}\left(\dfrac{2.5}{\sqrt{74}}\right) = 16.204...°$

So angle $BMF = 16.204... \times 2 = 32.4°$ (3 s.f.) *[1 mark]*

[3 marks available in total — as above]

There are other methods you could use here — e.g. you could find MB instead of MN and use that to find the angle.

6   Let X be the point 4 cm from D on the line DA.

Then AXB is a right angled triangle.

$BX^2 = 5^2 - (7 - 4)^2 = 16$ so $BX = 4$ cm $= DC$ *[1 mark]*

Now use this to work out all the sides of triangle DEG:

$DG^2 = 11^2 + 4^2 = 137$ so $DG = \sqrt{137}$ cm *[1 mark]*

$GE^2 = 4^2 + 7^2 = 65$ so $GE = \sqrt{65}$ cm *[1 mark]*

$DE^2 = 11^2 + 7^2 = 170$ so $DE = \sqrt{170}$ cm *[1 mark]*

Now use the cosine rule to find angle DEG:

$\cos DEG = \dfrac{\sqrt{170}^2 + \sqrt{65}^2 - \sqrt{137}^2}{2 \times \sqrt{170} \times \sqrt{65}} = 0.466...$

Angle $DEG = \cos^{-1}(0.466...) = 62.216...° = 62.2°$ (3 s.f.) *[1 mark]*

[5 marks available in total — as above]

7   $AN = 12 \times \dfrac{3}{4} = 9$ cm and $ND = 12 - 9 = 3$ cm *[1 mark for both]*

In triangle CNF: $CF = 12$ cm

$CN^2 = 8^2 + 9^2 + 4^2 = 161$ so $CN = \sqrt{161}$ cm *[1 mark]*

$NF^2 = 3^2 + 8^2 + 4^2 = 89$ so $NF = \sqrt{89}$ cm *[1 mark]*

Now use the cosine rule to find angle CNF:

$\cos CNF = \dfrac{\sqrt{161}^2 + \sqrt{89}^2 - 12^2}{2 \times \sqrt{161} \times \sqrt{89}}$ *[1 mark]* $= 0.442...$

Angle $CNF = \cos^{-1}(0.442...) = 63.719...° = 63.7°$ (1 d.p.) *[1 mark]*

[5 marks available in total — as above]

Pages 76-77: Vectors

1   Use the ratios given to label the shape:

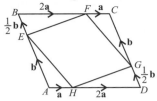

First work out $\overrightarrow{HG}$ and $\overrightarrow{EF}$:

$\overrightarrow{HG} = \overrightarrow{HD} + \overrightarrow{DG} = 2\mathbf{a} + \dfrac{1}{2}\mathbf{b}$ and $\overrightarrow{EF} = \overrightarrow{EB} + \overrightarrow{BF} = \dfrac{1}{2}\mathbf{b} + 2\mathbf{a}$

As $\overrightarrow{HG}$ and $\overrightarrow{EF}$ are the same vector, HG and EF are parallel lines.

Then work out $\overrightarrow{HE}$ and $\overrightarrow{GF}$:

$\overrightarrow{HE} = \overrightarrow{HA} + \overrightarrow{AE} = -\mathbf{a} + \mathbf{b}$ and $\overrightarrow{GF} = \overrightarrow{GC} + \overrightarrow{CF} = \mathbf{b} - \mathbf{a}$

As $\overrightarrow{HE}$ and $\overrightarrow{GF}$ are the same vector, HE and GF are parallel lines.

$EFGH$ has two pairs of parallel sides, so is a parallelogram.

[3 marks available — 1 mark for working out $\overrightarrow{HG}$ and $\overrightarrow{EF}$, 1 mark for working out $\overrightarrow{HE}$ and $\overrightarrow{GF}$, 1 mark for an explanation that the shape has two pairs of parallel lines so is a parallelogram]

2   a) PQD and ACD are similar, and $AD:PD = 5:3$,

so $\overrightarrow{CA} = \dfrac{5}{3} \times \overrightarrow{QP} = \dfrac{5}{3}\mathbf{b}$ *[1 mark]*

b) $\overrightarrow{PR} = \overrightarrow{PA} + \overrightarrow{AR}$

$AD:PD = 5:3$ so $AP:PD = 2:3$ and $3\overrightarrow{PA} = 2\overrightarrow{DP}$

$\overrightarrow{PA} = \dfrac{2}{3}\overrightarrow{DP} = \dfrac{2}{3}(-\mathbf{a} + \mathbf{b}) = -\dfrac{2}{3}\mathbf{a} + \dfrac{2}{3}\mathbf{b}$ *[1 mark]*

$\overrightarrow{AR} = \dfrac{2}{5}\overrightarrow{AC} = -\dfrac{2}{5}\overrightarrow{CA} = -\dfrac{2}{5} \times \dfrac{5}{3}\mathbf{b} = -\dfrac{2}{3}\mathbf{b}$ *[1 mark]*

$\overrightarrow{PR} = -\dfrac{2}{3}\mathbf{a} + \dfrac{2}{3}\mathbf{b} - \dfrac{2}{3}\mathbf{b} = -\dfrac{2}{3}\mathbf{a}$

$\overrightarrow{DQ} = -\mathbf{a}$ so $k = \dfrac{2}{3}$ *[1 mark]*

[3 marks available in total — as above]

3   E.g. $\overrightarrow{AC}$ and $\overrightarrow{AE}$ are parallel vectors as ACE is a straight line.

$\overrightarrow{AC} = k\mathbf{b} + 6\mathbf{a}$ *[1 mark]*

$\overrightarrow{AE} = \overrightarrow{AB} + \overrightarrow{BE} = 6\mathbf{a} + (4\mathbf{a} + 25\mathbf{b}) = 10\mathbf{a} + 25\mathbf{b}$ *[1 mark]*

Comparing the coefficients of $\mathbf{a}$, $\overrightarrow{AE} = \dfrac{10}{6}\overrightarrow{AC}$ *[1 mark]*

So $k = 25 \div \dfrac{10}{6} = 15$ *[1 mark]*

[4 marks available in total — as above]

There are other ways to solve this question — if you got the answer and showed your working then you'll get full marks.

4   E.g. $AB:BC:CD = 4:3:4$

$\overrightarrow{AB} = 3\mathbf{a}$, $\overrightarrow{BC} = 3\mathbf{a} \times \dfrac{3}{4} = \dfrac{9}{4}\mathbf{a}$ and $\overrightarrow{CD} = 3a$ *[1 mark]*

$\overrightarrow{FE} = \overrightarrow{CD} = 3\mathbf{a}$

$\overrightarrow{AE} = \overrightarrow{AF} + \overrightarrow{FE} = \left(\dfrac{15}{4}\mathbf{a} + 2\mathbf{b}\right) + 3\mathbf{a} = \dfrac{27}{4}\mathbf{a} + 2\mathbf{b}$ *[1 mark]*

$\overrightarrow{FC} = \overrightarrow{FA} + \overrightarrow{AC} = -\left(\dfrac{15}{4}\mathbf{a} + 2\mathbf{b}\right) + 3\mathbf{a} + \dfrac{9}{4}\mathbf{a} = \dfrac{3}{2}\mathbf{a} - 2\mathbf{b}$ *[1 mark]*

$4\overrightarrow{FM} = \overrightarrow{MC}$ so $\overrightarrow{FM} = \dfrac{1}{5}\overrightarrow{FC} = \dfrac{1}{5}\left(\dfrac{3}{2}\mathbf{a} - 2\mathbf{b}\right) = \dfrac{3}{10}\mathbf{a} - \dfrac{2}{5}\mathbf{b}$

$\overrightarrow{AM} = \overrightarrow{AF} + \overrightarrow{FM} = \left(\dfrac{15}{4}\mathbf{a} + 2\mathbf{b}\right) + \left(\dfrac{3}{10}\mathbf{a} - \dfrac{2}{5}\mathbf{b}\right)$

$\qquad\qquad = \dfrac{81}{20}\mathbf{a} + \dfrac{8}{5}\mathbf{b}$ *[1 mark]*

$\overrightarrow{AM}$ is not a scalar multiple of $\overrightarrow{AE}$ so they are not parallel and so AME is not a straight line. *[1 mark]*

[5 marks available in total — as above]

You could have shown that $\overrightarrow{AM}$ and $\overrightarrow{ME}$ aren't parallel instead.

Section 7 — Probability and Statistics

Pages 78-80: Probability

1   a)   Frequency of odd number $= 54 + 38 + 61 = 153$

Relative frequency of an odd number $= \dfrac{153}{200} = 0.765$

[2 marks available — 1 mark for a correct method, 1 mark for the correct answer]

b)   E.g. the relative frequency of getting a 5 is $\dfrac{61}{200} = 0.305$ which is less than 0.5, so he is actually unlikely to get a 5.

[1 mark for any valid explanation]

2 a) His first serve was in on 150 × 0.7 = 105 points.
So his first serve wasn't in on 150 – 105 = 45 points.
He won 105 × 0.8 = 84 points and lost 105 – 84 = 21 points
when his first serve was in.
He won 45 × 0.4 = 18 points and lost 45 – 18 = 27 points
when his first serve wasn't in.

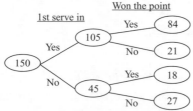

*[3 marks available — 3 marks for a fully correct frequency
tree, otherwise 2 marks for at least 5 values correct or
1 mark for at least 3 values correct]*

b) He won 84 + 18 = 102 points so the probability that he won a
randomly chosen point is $\frac{102}{150} = \frac{17}{25} = 0.68$

*[2 marks available — 1 mark for a correct method,
1 mark for the correct answer]*

3 For 1 scoop there are 16 combinations.
For 2 scoops there are 16 × 16 = 256 combinations *[1 mark]*.
For 3 scoops there are 16 × 16 × 16 = 4096 combinations *[1 mark]*.
4096 + 256 + 16 = 4368 so his statement is not correct *[1 mark]*.
[3 marks available in total — as above]

4 a) Let x = P(3). Then P(1) = $3x$, so P(odd) = $x + 3x = 4x$
P(even) = 2 × P(odd) = 2 × $4x$ = $8x$
P(even) + P(odd) = 1, so $4x + 8x = 12x = 1$
$x = \frac{1}{12}$, so P(3) = $\frac{1}{12}$

*[2 marks available — 1 mark for finding expressions
for the probabilities, 1 mark for the correct answer]*

b) P(1 even and 1 odd) = P(even, odd) + P(odd, even)
$= \left(\frac{2}{3} \times \frac{1}{3}\right) + \left(\frac{1}{3} \times \frac{2}{3}\right) = \frac{4}{9}$

*[2 marks available — 1 mark for a correct method,
1 mark for the correct answer]*

5 a) There are 20 possibilities for each number so there are
20 × 20 × 20 = 8000 combinations *[1 mark]*.

b) There are 8 prime numbers, 10 odd numbers
and 4 square numbers on the lock.
So there are 8 × 10 × 4 = 320 possible combinations.
Which is 8000 – 320 = 7680 fewer combinations.
The percentage decrease is $\frac{7680}{8000} \times 100 = 96\%$.

*[4 marks available — 1 mark for working out the number
choices for each number, 1 mark for working out the number
of possible combinations, 1 mark for the correct method to
find the percentage decrease, 1 mark for the correct answer]*

6 $G_A G_B = 0.24$ [1]

$G_A B_B = 0.56$ and $B_B = 1 - G_B$
So, $G_A(1 - G_B) = 0.56$, which means $G_A - G_A G_B = 0.56$ [2]
Substitute [1] into [2]: $G_A - 0.24 = 0.56$, so $G_A = 0.8$
Putting this value back into [1]: $0.8G_B = 0.24$, so $G_B = 0.3$
So in Year 9 there are (30 × 0.8) + (30 × 0.3) = 33 girls
*[4 marks available — 1 mark for forming the two simultaneous
equations, 1 mark for finding G_A, 1 mark for finding G_B,
1 mark for the correct answer]*

7 At the start, Bag A: P(red) = $\frac{n}{n+14}$ and Bag B: P(red) = $\frac{30}{30+n}$
When 2 blue balls are moved,
Bag A contains 12 blue and n red so P(red) = $\frac{n}{n+12}$ *[1 mark]*

Bag B contains 30 red and $n+2$ blue, so P(red) = $\frac{30}{n+32}$ *[1 mark]*

The probabilities are equal so: $\frac{n}{n+12} = \frac{30}{n+32}$
$n(n+32) = 30(n+12)$ *[1 mark]*
$n^2 + 32n = 30n + 360$
$n^2 + 2n - 360 = 0$ *[1 mark]*
$(n-18)(n+20) = 0$, so $n = 18$ (as n must be positive) *[1 mark]*
The original probability of picking a red ball from Bag B is
$\frac{30}{30+18} = \frac{30}{48} = \frac{5}{8}$ *[1 mark]*
[6 marks available in total — as above]

Pages 81-82: Tree Diagrams

1 a)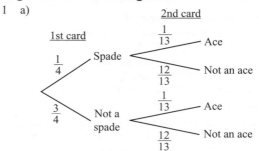

*[2 marks available in total — 2 marks for a fully correct tree
diagram, otherwise 1 mark for at least 3 correct probabilities]*

b) P(not a spade and not an ace) = $\frac{3}{4} \times \frac{12}{13} = \frac{36}{52} = \frac{9}{13}$ *[1 mark]*

For questions 2-4, you can draw tree diagrams to help you if you want.

2 a) There are 5 prime numbers between 1 and 12 so P(prime) = $\frac{5}{12}$
P(3 prime numbers) = P(prime) × P(prime) × P(prime)
$= \frac{5}{12} \times \frac{5}{12} \times \frac{5}{12} = \frac{125}{1728}$

*[2 marks available — 1 mark for the correct probability of
a prime number, 1 mark for the correct answer]*

b) P(roll < 5) = $\frac{1}{3}$ and P(roll ≥ 5) = $\frac{2}{3}$
P(one roll < 5) = P(1st number is < 5, other 2 are ≥ 5)
+ P(2nd number is < 5, other 2 are ≥ 5)
+ P(3rd number is < 5, other 2 are ≥ 5)
P (one roll < 5) = $\left(\frac{1}{3} \times \frac{2}{3} \times \frac{2}{3}\right) + \left(\frac{2}{3} \times \frac{1}{3} \times \frac{2}{3}\right) + \left(\frac{2}{3} \times \frac{2}{3} \times \frac{1}{3}\right)$
$= \frac{12}{27} = \frac{4}{9}$

*[3 marks available — 1 mark for the correct probabilities for
less than a 5 and 5 or more, 1 mark for a correct method for
finding the answer, 1 mark for the correct answer]*

3 P(less than 5 fish) = 1 – P(5 or more fish)
P(5 or more fish) = P(1, 2, 2) + P(2, 1, 2) + P(2, 2, 1) + P(2, 2, 2)
= (0.5 × 0.3 × 0.3) + (0.3 × 0.5 × 0.3) + (0.3 × 0.3 × 0.5)
+ (0.3 × 0.3 × 0.3) = 0.045 + 0.045 + 0.045 + 0.027 = 0.162
P(less than 5 fish) = 1 – 0.162 = 0.838
*[4 marks available in total — 1 mark for finding the outcomes
that will give 5 or more fish, 1 mark for calculating the
probability of each of the outcomes, 1 mark for adding the
probabilities together, 1 mark for the correct answer]*

4 a) There are 6 × 6 = 36 possible outcomes and there are three
ways to win the game (rolling a 5 and 6, 6 and 5, or 6 and 6).
So the probability of winning is $\frac{3}{36} = \frac{1}{12}$.
So you'd estimate that a prize will be won every 12 games.
If there are 20 prizes, you'd estimate that the stall will run out
of prizes after 12 × 20 = 240 games.
It takes £2 each go, so expected takings are 240 × £2 = £480.
*[3 marks available — 1 mark for finding the number of
winning outcomes, 1 mark for the correct probability of
winning, 1 mark for explaining why this means you'd estimate
240 games will be played and therefore £480 will be taken]*

b) P(wins at least one prize) = 1 – P(no prizes)
P(no prizes) = $\frac{11}{12} \times \frac{11}{12} = \frac{121}{144}$ *[1 mark]*
P(wins at least one prize) = 1 – $\frac{121}{144}$ *[1 mark]* = $\frac{23}{144}$ *[1 mark]*
[3 marks available in total — as above]

Pages 83-84: Conditional Probability

1   P(both the same) = P(chocolate, chocolate) + P(plain, plain)
$$= \left(\frac{8}{14} \times \frac{7}{13}\right) + \left(\frac{6}{14} \times \frac{5}{13}\right) = \frac{43}{91}$$
[3 marks available — 1 mark for finding the outcomes where both biscuits are the same, 1 mark for working out the probabilities of these outcomes, 1 mark for the correct answer]

2   a)   P(one C and one S) = P(C, S) + P(S, C)
$$= \left(\frac{5}{12} \times \frac{3}{11}\right) + \left(\frac{3}{12} \times \frac{5}{11}\right) = \frac{5}{22}$$
[3 marks available — 1 mark for finding the outcomes where one tub is chocolate and one tub is strawberry, 1 mark for working out the probabilities of these outcomes, 1 mark for the correct answer]

   b)   P(at least one V) = 1 − P(no V's)
$$P(\text{no V's}) = \left(\frac{8}{12} \times \frac{7}{11}\right) = \frac{56}{132} = \frac{14}{33} \ \textit{[1 mark]}$$
$$P(\text{at least one V}) = 1 - \frac{14}{33} \ \textit{[1 mark]} = \frac{19}{33} \ \textit{[1 mark]}$$
[3 marks available in total — as above]

3   P(aerobics) = 0.4 , P(not aerobics) = 1 − 0.4 = 0.6 and
P(run given not aerobics) = 0.7,
P(not run given not aerobics) = 1 − 0.7 = 0.3
P(not run and not aerobics)
= P(not aerobics) × P(not run given not aerobics) = 0.6 × 0.3
$$= 0.18.$$
[3 marks available — 1 mark for finding the missing probabilities, 1 mark for putting the numbers into the formula correctly, 1 mark for the correct answer]
You could have done this one using a tree diagram instead.

4   a)   P(at least one prize) = 1 − P(no prizes)
20 tickets end in a 0 or 5 so the probability of picking a winning ticket is $\frac{20}{100}$ and a losing ticket is $\frac{80}{100}$. *[1 mark]*
$$P(\text{no prizes}) = \frac{80}{100} \times \frac{79}{99} = \frac{316}{495} \ \textit{[1 mark]}$$
$$P(\text{at least one prize}) = 1 - \frac{316}{495} \ \textit{[1 mark]} = \frac{179}{495} \ \textit{[1 mark]}$$
[4 marks available in total — as above]

   b)   There are 100 − 40 = 60 tickets left and 20 − 5 = 15 of them are winning tickets so the probability of picking a winning ticket is $\frac{15}{60}$ and a losing ticket is $\frac{45}{60}$.
$$P(\text{no prizes}) = \frac{45}{60} \times \frac{44}{59} = \frac{33}{59}$$
$$P(\text{at least one prize}) = 1 - \frac{33}{59} = \frac{26}{59} = 0.440...$$
$$\frac{179}{495} = 0.361...$$
0.440... > 0.361... so her chances of winning are better than Amy's.
[3 marks available in total — 1 mark for working out the probability of picking a losing ticket, 1 mark for calculating the probability of Carla winning at least one prize, 1 mark for saying she has a better chance to win by comparing the fractions]

5   $P(\text{picking a green counter}) = \frac{n}{n + (n+1)} = \frac{n}{2n+1}$ *[1 mark]*
$P(\text{picking a blue counter}) = \frac{n+1}{n + (n+1)} = \frac{n+1}{2n+1}$ *[1 mark]*
$P(\text{picking 2 green counters}) = \frac{n}{2n+1} \times \frac{n-1}{2n} = \frac{n-1}{4n+2}$ *[1 mark]*
$P(\text{picking 2 blue counters}) = \frac{n+1}{2n+1} \times \frac{n}{2n} = \frac{n+1}{4n+2}$ *[1 mark]*
$P(\text{both counters are the same}) = \frac{n-1}{4n+2} + \frac{n+1}{4n+2}$
$$= \frac{2n}{4n+2} = \frac{n}{2n+1} \ \textit{[1 mark]}$$
[5 marks available in total — as above]

Pages 85-86: Venn Diagrams

1   a)   2n + 1 generates set A = {3, 5, 7, 9, 11, 13, 15, 17, 19}
$\frac{n(n+1)}{2}$ generates set B = {1, 3, 6, 10, 15}
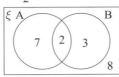
[3 marks available — 3 marks for a completely correct Venn diagram, otherwise 1 mark for listing or finding the number of elements in set A and 1 mark for listing or finding the number of elements in set B]

   b) $\frac{2}{20} = \frac{1}{10}$ *[1 mark]*

2   a)   106 + 19 = 125 students attend the disco
106 + 19 + 33 + 42 = 200 students in total.
125 : 200 *[1 mark]* = 5 : 8 *[1 mark]*
[2 marks available in total — as above]

   b)   (i) $\frac{19}{125}$
[2 marks available — 1 mark for the correct numerator, 1 mark for the correct denominator]

      (ii) $\frac{106}{139}$
[2 marks available — 1 mark for the correct numerator, 1 mark for the correct denominator]

3   a)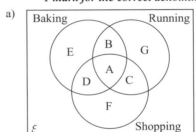
A: 10% of 80 = 0.1 × 80 = 8 *[1 mark]*
B: 22 − 8 = 14   C: 18 − 8 = 10 *[1 mark for both]*
Half the people only liked 1 activity so the other half liked 2 or 3 activities: 0.5 × 80 = 40.
D: 40 − (14 + 10 + 8) = 8 *[1 mark]*
E: 43 − (14 + 8 + 8) = 13
F: 35 − (8 + 8 + 10) = 9 *[1 mark for both E and F]*
G: 80 − (8 + 14 + 10 + 8 + 13 + 9) = 18 *[1 mark]*
[5 marks available in total — as above]

   b) $\frac{14+8+8}{14+8+8+10} = \frac{30}{40} = \frac{3}{4}$
[2 marks available — 1 mark for correct calculation, 1 mark for the correct answer]

4   There are 50 people in the choir, so
n(n + 2) + n + (2n − 3) + (8 − n) = 50 *[1 mark]*
$n^2 + 4n + 5 = 50$, so $n^2 + 4n - 45 = 0$
(n + 9)(n − 5) = 0, so n = 5 (as n has to be positive) *[1 mark]*
The number of people who play the piano is
n(n + 2) + n = (5 × 7) + 5 = 40 *[1 mark]*
$P(\text{both play piano}) = \frac{40}{50} \times \frac{39}{49} \ \textit{[1 mark]} = \frac{156}{245} \ \textit{[1 mark]}$
[5 marks available in total — as above]

Pages 87-88: Histograms

1   70 < t ≤ 85 has a frequency of 39. Class width = 85 − 70 = 15.
The frequency density for the class 70 < t ≤ 85 is 39 ÷ 15 = 2.6, so
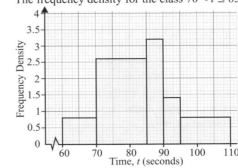

Time t (seconds)	Frequency
$60 < t \leq 70$	$10 \times 0.8 = 8$
$70 < t \leq 85$	$15 \times 2.6 = 39$
$85 < t \leq 90$	$5 \times 3.2 = 16$
$90 < t \leq 95$	$5 \times 1.4 = 7$
$95 < t \leq 110$	$15 \times 0.8 = 12$

Total number of members = 8 + 39 + 16 + 7 + 12 = 82
[4 marks available in total — 1 mark for finding the frequency density of the $70 < t \leq 85$ class, 1 mark for using this to find the frequency densities of the other classes, 1 mark for finding the frequencies of each class, 1 mark for the correct answer]

2 a) Start by working out the frequency of bouncy balls in each class: The whole histogram represents 600 bouncy balls and there are 30 big squares in the histogram so each big square represents 600 ÷ 30 = 20 bouncy balls.

Weight w (grams)	Frequency
$40 < w \leq 41$	$20 \times 4 = 80$
$41 < w \leq 41.5$	$20 \times 4 = 80$
$41.5 < w \leq 42.5$	$20 \times 6 = 120$
$42.5 < w \leq 43.5$	$20 \times 12 = 240$
$43.5 < w \leq 44$	$20 \times 4 = 80$

To estimate the mean, first multiply the mid-point of each class by the frequency:
$(40.5 \times 80) + (41.25 \times 80) + (42 \times 120)$
$+ (43 \times 240) + (43.75 \times 80) = 25\,400$
So mean = 25 400 ÷ 600 = 42.3333...= 42.3 g (to 1 d.p.)
[5 marks available — 1 mark for a correct method to work out the frequency of each class, 1 mark for the correct frequencies for each class, 1 mark for multiplying the mid-points of each class by the frequencies, 1 mark for dividing by 600 to find the mean, 1 mark for the correct answer]

b) E.g. The median weight is between the 300th and 301st ball, which are both in the class $42.5 < w \leq 43.5$ so Sumi is correct.
[2 marks available — 1 mark for saying she is correct, 1 mark for a correct explanation]

3 a) The frequencies are given by the area of each bar.

Height (metres)	Frequency
1 to 2	$1 \times 12 = 12$
2 to 2.5	$0.5 \times 32 = 16$
2.5 to 2.75	$0.25 \times 88 = 22$
2.75 to 3	$0.25 \times 72 = 18$
3 to 4	$1 \times 12 = 12$

[1 mark]
Total = 12 + 16 + 22 + 18 + 12 = 80
Estimate of number of statues between 1.75 m to 2.75 m
= ((2 − 1.75) × 12) + 16 + 22 = 41 *[1 mark]*
Percentage = (41 ÷ 80) × 100 = 51.25% *[1 mark]*
[3 marks available in total — as above]

b) To estimate the mean height, first multiply the midpoint of each interval by the frequency:
$(1.5 \times 12) + (2.25 \times 16) + (2.625 \times 22)$
$+ (2.875 \times 18) + (3.5 \times 12)$
= 18 + 36 + 57.75 + 51.75 + 42 = 205.5
Estimate of mean = 205.5 ÷ 80
= 2.57 metres (2 d.p.) which is more than 2.5 metres.
[3 marks available in total — 1 mark for multiplying the mid-points of each class by the frequencies, 1 mark for dividing by 80 to find the mean, 1 mark for the correct answer]

c) There are 16 + 22 + 18 + 12 = 68 statues over 2 metres.
There are 12 statues over 3 metres.
P(over 3 metres given it is over 2 metres) = $\frac{12}{68} = \frac{3}{17}$.
[2 marks available — 1 mark for correct calculation, 1 mark for the correct answer]

Pages 89-90: Comparing Data Sets

1 The tickets took 30 minutes to sell out in 2013 but only 24 minutes in 2014 so they sold out quicker in 2014.
The median in 2013 was 12.5 minutes. So the first half of the tickets sold out quicker in 2013 then slowed down, whereas in 2014, sales started slowly then sped up.
The interquartile range in 2013 was 15.5 – 10 = 5.5 minutes and in 2014 it was 3 minutes. Ticket sales were more concentrated around the median time in 2014 as the interquartile range is smaller.
[4 marks available — 1 mark for comparing the times it took the tickets to sell out, 1 mark for finding and comparing the medians, 1 mark for working out the interquartile range in 2013, 1 mark for comparing the interquartile ranges]

2 a)

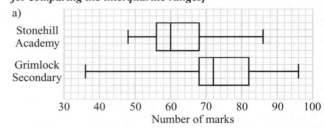

[2 marks available — 2 marks for a fully correct box plot, otherwise 1 mark for correctly showing at least 3 of lower endpoint, upper endpoint, median, lower quartile and upper quartile]

b) The median is higher at Grimlock Secondary so on average their GCSE maths pupils scored higher. The range and interquartile range are both smaller at Stonehill Academy so their GCSE maths pupils scored more consistent marks.
[2 marks available — 1 mark for comparing the medians with a valid explanation, 1 mark for comparing the ranges or interquartile ranges with a correct explanation]

3 a) (i) E.g. The maximum range of house prices in town A is £360 000 – £200 000 = £160 000.
The minimum range of house prices in town B is £340 000 – £180 000 = £160 000.
So the statement is incorrect the range of house prices in town A cannot be greater than the range for town B.
[2 marks available — 1 mark for working out the range of house prices in each town, 1 mark for a correct comparison]

(ii) E.g. It is impossible to tell — the histogram doesn't have a scale on the frequency density axis. You can only tell the proportion of houses in certain price brackets, not the number of houses.
[2 marks available — 1 mark for saying you can't tell this from the histogram, 1 mark for a correct explanation]

b) Work out the proportion of houses between £280 000 and £320 000 in each town by counting the number of squares of the histogram they take up.
In town A: 8 big squares are between £280 000 and £320 000. There are 24 squares in the histogram. The proportion of houses between £280 000 and £320 000 is $\frac{8}{24} = \frac{1}{3}$.
In town B: 10 big squares are between £280 000 and £320 000. There are 40 squares in the histogram. The proportion of houses between £280 000 and £320 000 is $\frac{10}{40} = \frac{1}{4}$.
$\frac{1}{3} > \frac{1}{4}$ so there is a higher proportion of houses between £280 000 and £320 000 in town A.
[4 marks available in total — 1 mark for the correct method to work out the proportions, 1 mark for the correct proportion for town A, 1 mark for the correct proportion for town B, 1 mark for the correct answer]